arts activities for children at bedside
Judy Rollins

Art Director
David Boyle

Photography
Mike Rollins

Forward by L. Lawrence Riccio

WVSA arts connection
1100 16th Street, NW
Washington, DC 20036
v 202.296.9100
tty 202.261.0201
f 202.261.0200
www.wvsarts.org

ISBN 0-931678-08-1

tableofcontents

Forward vi

Acknowledgements ix

Preface x

Introduction xiii

01. **Saying Hello** 1

Pop-up Card 3

Magic Heart 6

Little Book 7

02. **Bringing the Outside In** 9

The View from the Window 12

Weaving on Fallen Tree Branches 14

Sandcast Candles 16

Sidewalk 20

Leaf Prints on Fabric 22

03. **Images** 25

Drawing 27

Mandalas 30

Moment Boards 33

Marble Painting 35

Silkscreen Circle Prints 37

Bubble Paintings 40

Life Necklace 44

Personal Containers 47

04. **Words 49**

Getting Started 51

Poetry 54

Storytelling 57

05. **Sounds 61**

Musical Instruments 64

Singing 68

Wind Chimes 71

06. **Movement 73**

Movement Conversation 75

Mirroring 78

In the Ring 80

Shadow Drama 83

Puppet Drama 84

07. **Light** 87

In the Room 89

What is It? 91

Polaroid Image Transfer 93

Light Show 95

Glow in the Dark 98

08. **Around the World** 101

Chinese Paper Batiks 103

Japanese Garden Theatre 108

Aboriginal Dreamtime Painting 110

French Divisionalism 113

09. **Going Through the Day** 117

Daily Care 119

Mealtime 123

The Medical Environment 127

The Hardest Part 131

Treatment Regimes 135

A Final Note 141

References 144

Appendix A: A Selection of Ethnic and Religious Festivals 147

Appendix B: Art Materials and Projects for Children and Other High-Risk Individuals 149

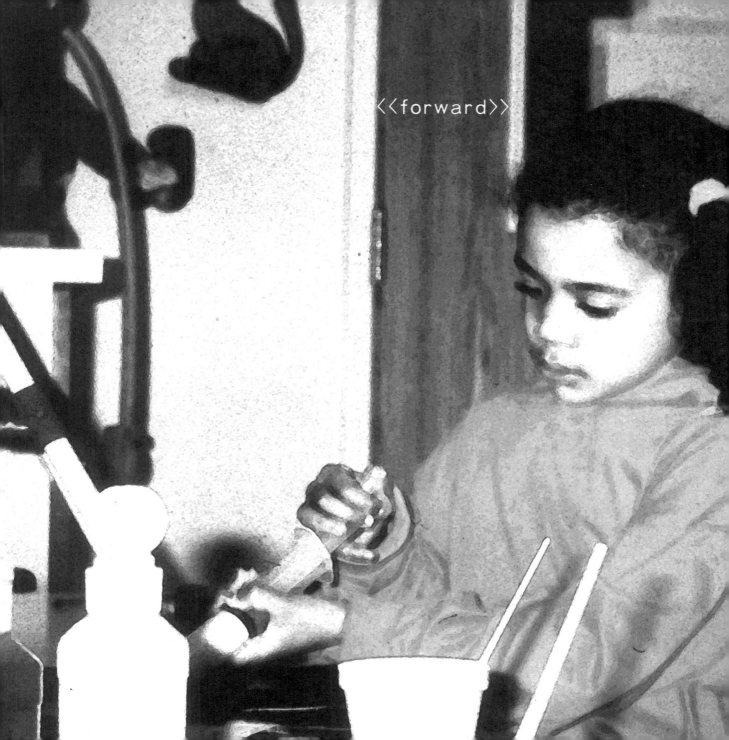

The arts can play an important role in our lives from birth until death. They can shape lives, define our communities, increase quality of life, and make for quality education. Throughout our lives we see many instances of the arts touching people on an emotional level and connecting them through shared experiences.

Although arts and healthcare have been companions probably since the beginning of humankind, today's changing landscape has created greater demands for both those in need of care and the caregivers (Wikoff, 2003). There are at least four areas where the arts have a significant role to play in healthcare: (a) by enhancing the healthcare environment; (b) by providing a therapeutic tool for patients; (c) by serving as "therapy" for health professionals; and (d) by aiding public understanding of health issues (Rice, 2003).

Arts Activities for Children at Bedside draws upon Judy Rollins' 30+ years experience in arts-in-healthcare with children, their families, and caregivers. Under her direction, WVSA arts connection has spearheaded programming in all four of the areas Rice describes. WVSA artists enhance hospital environments through murals, music, and the performing arts; and engage in the therapeutic use of the arts with children and their families through the "Studio G" program at Georgetown University Hospital, and the "ART is the heART" program at Hospital for Sick Children, Washington Hospice, and in the homes of children and families in home and hospice care. Veterans at the VA Medical Center enjoy WVSA's visual arts and music programs. Through a for-credit course, "Arts for Children in Hospitals," medical students at Georgetown University School of Medicine learn about the importance of the arts for children who are hospitalized as well as ways to stay connected to their creative selves as they go out into the world as practicing physicians. Innovative federally-funded health education programs, such as WVSA's "Get the Lead Out" that targets childhood lead posioning, and the "Giant Food Guide Pyramid" project, have addressed health issues by using the arts to aid public understanding. (For more information about these and other WVSA programs, see http: //www.wvsarts.org)

Programs Dr. Rollins has developed are respected and replicated nationally and internationally because they incorporate sound psychosocial principles of pediatric healthcare. *Arts Activities for Children at Bedside* reflects this sensitivity. My wish is that this book will help artists and others who use it recognize that they can do much more than simply help a child

pass the time; they can make that time have true and enduring meaning.

L. Lawrence Riccio, EdD
President/CEO
WVSA arts connection

<<Acknowledgements>>

I would like to thank Johnson & Johnson and the Society for the Arts in Healthcare for their support in funding the development and production of *Arts Activities for Children at Bedside*. I am also most grateful to the artists from ART is the heART, Studio G, and from around the world who contributed activities and ideas, and to the wonderful children and families who participated in testing them.

The creative team for this book—David Boyle and Mike Rollins— worked long and hard to help assure that the book's appearance was as exciting as its contents. As Art Director, David patiently listened to my ideas about the concept of the book, added many of his own, and then made the concept come to life. Mike spent endless hours shooting photographs of children and activities, and provided all of the photography for the book except for those photographs on pages 58 (David Boyle), 25, 128, 130, 142 (Joan Drescher), 97 (Nina Favata), vi, 64, 65, 66, 117 (Judy Rollins), 43, 44, 45, and 46 (Sinduri), to whom I also am most grateful.

Finally, I would like to express my gratitude to L. Lawrence Riccio, WVSA arts connection's CEO/President, for his encouragement and support.

"What do you mean, you've come by to see if my child would like to dance?" a bewildered parent asks. "He can't even get out of bed."

Of course children can dance while in bed, as well as do many other things. Sometimes it means redefining terms such as "dance." Other times it means adapting an activity to meet children where they are at the moment. But, ultimately, even very sick children or children who are dying can participate in arts activities at bedside.

As the arts-in-healthcare movement extends to all corners of the globe, artists working with children at the bedside in healthcare settings—be it in the hospital or home—are eager for ideas for activities. They are especially concerned with issues such as how a dancer can have a child "dance" while confined to a bed, what techniques a poet can use, or what supplies are safe to use with children in isolation following procedures such as bone marrow transplantation.

Arts Activities for Children at Bedside provides a sampling of activities that artists and other caring individuals can facilitate with children at bedside. The book's intent is not to be an exhaustive text of activities, but rather is to serve as a means to promote awareness and understanding of the exciting possibilities that exist. From this awareness and understanding, artists can develop their own repertoires that consider their talents and skills and the needs of the children they serve.

We are most grateful to Johnson & Johnson and the Society for the Arts in Healthcare for their generous grant that has made the development and publication of this book possible. We thank them in the name of the many

children that we hope will benefit
from this little book over the years
that follow.

Judy Rollins, PhD, RN
January 2004

<<introduction>>

How exciting that you are interested in bringing the arts to children at bedside. Whether in the hospital, clinic, home, or hospice care setting, healthcare experiences can be stressful for anyone, but can be especially so for children. However, with appropriate support, children can survive and even grow from such experiences. We now know that the arts can play a significant role in that support.

Selecting Activities

When planning activities for children at bedside, certain factors should be considered. For example, it is usually important to have some background information about the child, such as

- age
- reason for hospitalization or bed rest
- length of time the child is expected to be hospitalized or in bed
- condition, illness, or injury and the child's level of knowledge or understanding
- physical effects (e.g., nausea, sleepiness, loss of hair)
- interests
- present mood
- activity restrictions
- recent or upcoming experiences—good or bad
- physical limitations— temporary or permanent
- cognitive disabilities

Although the importance of maintaining confidentiality regarding patient information has always been stressed, the federal privacy standards— Health Insurance Portability and Accountability Act of 1996 (HIPAA), which went into effect in April 2003, have made healthcare providers more aware of the need to limit access to patient information. Therefore, you may only be provided with partial information, such as the patient's name, room number, physical limitations, mood or temperament, and any important safety issues. And, quite honestly, although it might be helpful to know more, this is really all the information that you need to provide an exciting and safe arts experience for a child.

From time to time we mention the specific age of a child who has especially enjoyed a particular activity; however, ages are not given throughout this book for several reasons:

1. A child often regresses when ill or hospitalized and therefore age ranges may be misleading.
2. The child's condition is often more of a factor in choice of activity than the child's age. What the child is capable of doing one day may differ dramatically from what he or she can do the next.
3. The majority of activities presented here can be taken "up or down" to meet a child's needs at the time.
4. A child who is physically unable to perform certain steps of an activity may nevertheless derive a great deal of pleasure in addition to therapeutic benefit from making creative choices and decisions and directing the artist to execute them.

Our artists often base activities on seasonal or holiday themes, which adds other benefits for the child. Participating in theme activities such as making Valentine cards in February helps to "normalize" the environment for the child; children who are not ill or hospitalized will be making Valentine cards as well. A theme activity also can provide an excellent method for learning about the world outside, e.g., different countries, customs, religions. For some themes to consider, we have included a listing of a selection of ethnic and religious festivals in Appendix A.

Safety is another important consideration. With any activity it is necessary to think through the safety issues and develop strategies to address them. For example, is there enough space to carry out the activity? (Some hospital over-bed tables are as small as 36" by 16".) Will this activity be excessively noisy and perhaps disturb others? Are the required materials and techniques safe for use with the child based upon his or her age, developmental level, or condition? A good rule is whenever there is any doubt, ask the child's doctor, nurse, child life specialist, or parent. A summary of art materials and safe alternatives can be found in Appendix B.

Infection Control

Special considerations are needed if you will be working with children who may be at increased risk for infection. For example, children with cancer are particularly susceptible to overwhelming, life-threatening infection at the time of diagnosis and/or relapse, during immunosuppressive therapy, and after prolonged antibiotic therapy. With the exception of children undergoing bone marrow transplantation, strict and formal "reverse" isolation of these children from others is becoming less common now than in the past (Kline, 2000). However, children are cautioned to avoid crowded areas and individuals who are ill, and their environment—whether in the hospital or at home—should be kept as clean as possible.

What does this mean for the artist? First, if you are ill, or even think that you may be getting a cold, flu, or other infection, postpone your visit. Second, wash your hands often. Third, always keep a stash of new, unopened supplies, e.g., paint sets, playdough, crayons, to use with children at risk for infection. And, lastly, ask the child's parent, doctor, nurse, or child life specialist before bringing anything into the child's room. Seemingly innocent items such as fruits and vegetables for printmaking may carry organisms that can be devastating for certain children.

In other instances, a child's condition may pose a risk for others, resulting in isolation of the child. Hospital staff will instruct you regarding the necessary precautions, such as hand washing technique and the use of gowns, gloves, masks, etc. If you must wear a mask, be sure to give the child the opportunity to see your face through a window or briefly at the door before donning the mask.

Being in isolation means sensory deprivation and depersonalization due to reduced interaction with the environment and the people in it. Also, isolation can have a significant impact on a child's orientation to time and place. Arts activities that provide sensory stimulation, stimulate kinesthesia, promote orientation to time and place, encourage social interactions, and reduce depersonalization are likely to be well-received by children in isolation (Hart, Mather, Slack, & Powell, 1992). You will find many activities within this book that offer such experiences.

Facilitating the Activities

Many activities in hospital settings take place in the playroom or other activity area. Often children can be brought to the area in their beds so that they, too, can enjoy the additional social aspects of participating in a group activity or working alongside other children.

Whether working with a group of children or an individual child, our artists live by the rule to never bring up the topic of the child's illness or condition. Some children want to use the time with an artist to escape their illness, to try to forget about it for a while. However, if the child initiates the topic, then the artist can join in. It is all about choice—the child's choice.

Finally, remember that a finished product is not an essential component of a successful creative experience. The creative process itself is valuable and memories of the process can survive a lifetime.

The Activities

Activities in *Arts Activities for Children at Bedside* are presented in nine topic areas:

01—*Saying Hello* activities are used to engage interest, break the ice, and provide an opportunity for the artist to begin to know the child and give the child an opportunity to get to know the artist.

02—*Bringing the Outside In* activities bring the world outside to the child's bedside.

03—*Images* presents visual arts activities as well as examples of the impact of images in the healthcare environment upon children.

04—*Words* introduces a variety of writing activities and storytelling.

05—*Sounds* offers music activities including instructions for making simple musical instruments.

06—*Movement* presents bedside dance and movement activities.

07—*Light* offers photography as an artistic medium and light as an art itself.

08—*Around the World* looks at a sampling of multicultural arts activities.

09—*Going Through the Day* consists of activities that caring individuals—parents, nurses, child life specialists, play specialists, social workers, chaplains—can incorporate into the child's daily care and medical regimes.

A Final Word offers some closing thoughts.

References includes literature cited in the text.

Appendix A—*A Selection of Ethnic and Religious Festivals* offers a month-by-month listing of ethnic and religious holidays from around the world.

Appendix B—*Art Materials and Projects for Children and Other High-Risk Individuals* provides essential safety information about art materials and techniques and suggested substitutions.

Afterwards

Children's artistic achievements should be celebrated. Their work can be displayed—not just on the hospital ward or unit, but in other places, such as the hospital cafeteria or lobby, a community museum or library, or even the local shopping mall. Framing or matting their paintings or drawings, creating simple anthologies of their poetry or stories, taping their songs, and taking pictures are all ways to let children know that their achievements are valued.

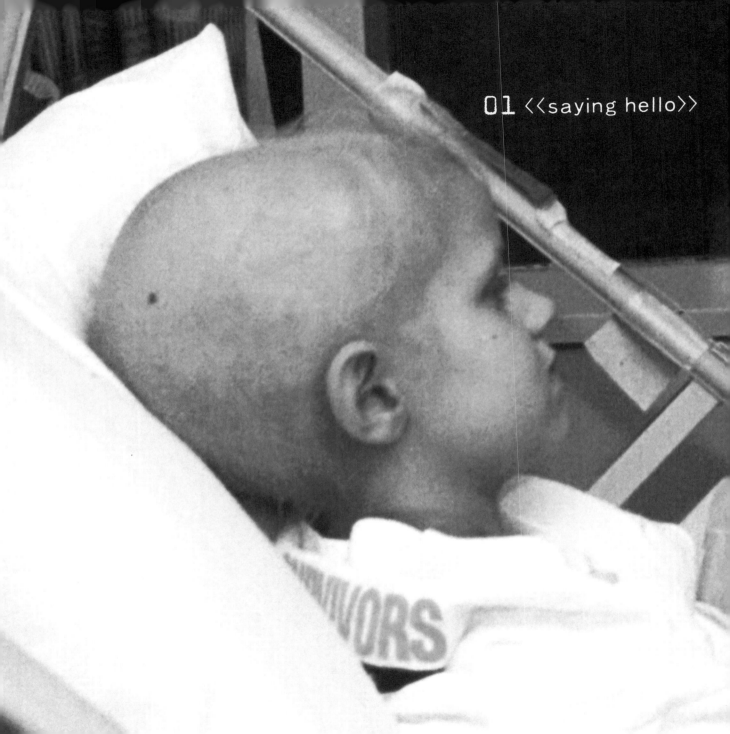

01 ⟨⟨saying hello⟩⟩

Imagine being in bed in a hospital room and the door opens. In walks another one of the many strangers that come into your room each day. What are your first thoughts? For most children it is "Who are you and what are you going to do to me?"

So, as an artist walking in, answering those two questions straight away is very important. But then what? What are some simple things that you can do to spark interest and develop rapport?

Each art medium tends to have its own method. For instance, visual artists will often show an example of the product of the art activity for the day, and musicians typically ask what kind of music the child likes.

But there also are some simple little things that artists of any kind can do. These activities can be used to engage interest, break the ice, and begin to get to know the child and give the child an opportunity to know you.

"Saying Hello" activities can stand on their own or can provide an introduction to a more extensive activity. These activities also are appropriate if you only have a few minutes to spend with a child. Each takes only a moment or two and requires simple materials that are usually already on hand.

Pop-up Card

The first time we used this activity was at Easter and many children made chicks. However, the "mouth" also suggests other birds, fish, or an imaginary animal. We usually demonstrate one step at a time and have the child follow along.

Materials
Paper or card stock
Scissors
Colored markers, colored pencils, crayons, paint

Process
1. Fold a sheet of paper in half, long ends together.
2. Fold the paper in half again in the other direction.
3. Grasp the gutter fold from the inside.
4. Cut a slit about 1" long wherever you would like the mouth to be.
5. Fold along a line from the end of the slit to the gutter crease, creating a triangle.
6. Fold it again in the other direction.
7. Repeat, creating a triangle on the other side of the slit.
8. Unfold the triangles, then unfold the gutter crease, opening out the card completely.
9. Pull up the triangle while also folding the card shut.
10. Close the pop-up, pressing it flat to strengthen the creases.
11. Using the pop-up area as the mouth, create an animal and scene.

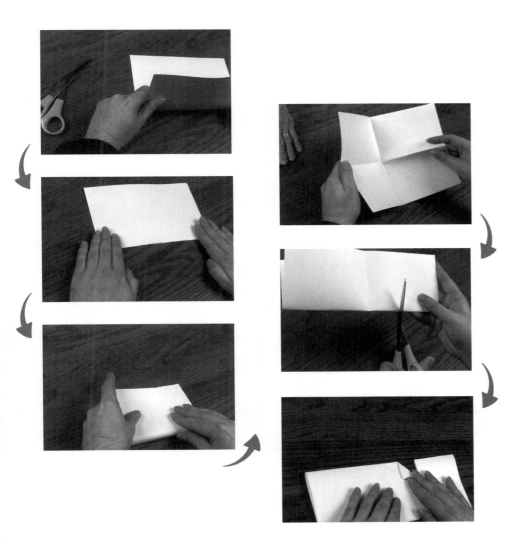

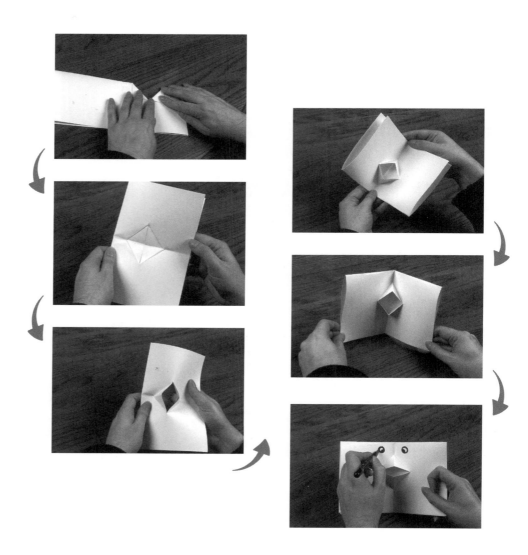

Magic Heart

We like to do this around Valentine's Day. The activity can be simply a fun thing that the child can later share with family and friends or it can provide a starting point for a discussion of or experimentation with other complementary colors for a child who expresses an interest in art.

Materials
Green felt tip marker, crayon, or colored pencil
Two pieces of white paper

Process
1. Ask the child to draw one or more hearts on one piece of paper.
2. Have the child color the heart(s) in green.
3. After it is filled in, ask the child to stare at it for about 30 seconds or more.
4. Then ask the child to look at the blank piece of paper. Depending upon the intensity of the green, a red or pink heart will appear.

Little Book

For centuries people have made books from all sorts of material and in all shapes and sizes. Although most books today are printed in large numbers and are bound mechanically, some are made by hand. A handmade book is special in that you probably won't find another one like it anywhere in the world. This simple little book can be used for telling stories, expressing feelings, and sharing ideas.

Materials
Paper or card stock
Scissors

Process
1. Fold the paper over longways so that the corners meet. Crease well and then unfold.
2. Fold the paper over in the other direction. Place the corners together and crease well. Do not unfold. Fold back one side as shown. Place the corners together and crease well.
3. Repeat with the other side.
4. Unfold the last two folds. Holding the folded side in your hand, cut along the center line until you reach the first vertical fold.
5. Open the paper so that eight sections are showing.
6. Fold the page over longways.
7. Holding on to each side, gently push the ends together to form the pages of the book.
8. Fold the front and back covers around so that the corners meet. Crease well. You should have six pages inside for writing and artwork.

02 bringing the outside in

Being outdoors can have a remarkably positive impact on a child's spirits, and whenever possible the child in bed should be taken outside, bed and all. Even opening the window can create a sense of being outside. However, in many instances, neither option is possible or advisable. Under these circumstances, the outdoors can be brought to the child. For example, in the winter, try bringing in a bowl of fresh snow for the child to make snow sculptures.

The arts provide many wonderful opportunities to bring the world outside to the child's bedside. In planning "outdoor" activities, consider the following factors:

- What is the season?
- What is the weather like today?
- What outdoor activities are children engaged in this time of year?

- What outdoor activities does the child like?
- What can the child see from his or her window?
- What is going on in nature (e.g., leaves changing colors, flowers blooming)?
- What natural resources are available?
- Are there restrictions regarding materials that the child can use?

With the answers to these questions, you can be on your way to helping to "normalize" the environment by bringing the outside in.

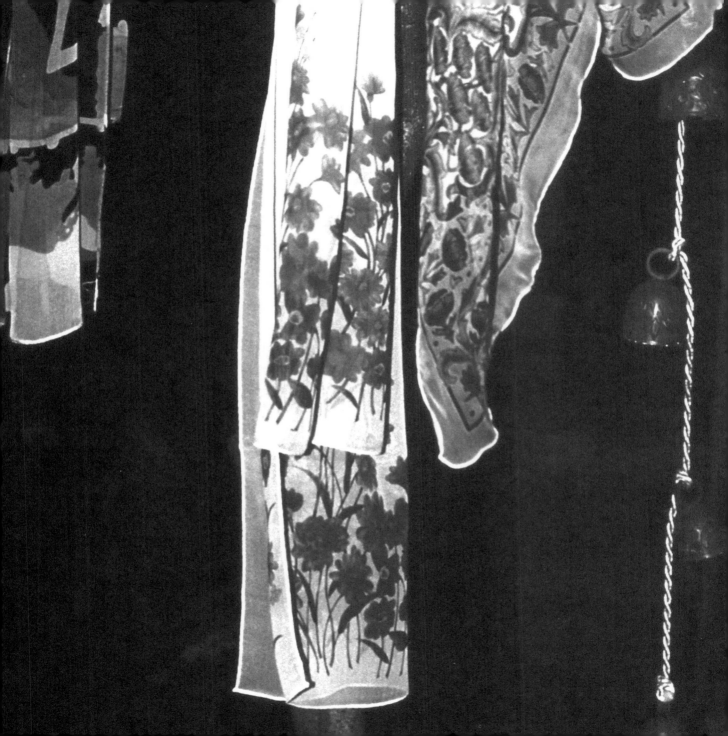

The view from the Window

What does the child see from the window? Research has demonstrated that views of nature may reduce stress and therefore support healing (Urich, 1984). The child at home in bed may have a lovely view of a favorite tree. The child's view from the hospital room may contain few elements of nature. In either case, the arts can be used to enhance the view from the window. Both sets of circumstances will be addressed below.

A Favorite Tree
Materials
Depends upon the project

Process
1. Help the child build and/or paint a birdhouse and hang it on the tree.
2. Have the child string round pieces of cereal with holes on yarn and tie it to a tree branch as a bird feeder.
3. Ask the child to select from a collection of scraps of silk or other light fabric and tie them to tree branches to allow the breeze to create a moving sculpture.
4. Help the child make wind chimes from clay (see 05 Sounds), sea shells, and old silverware, jewelry, or other found objects to hang from a tree branch.

Limited View of Nature
Materials
Tempera paint
Paintbrushes

Process

1. Ask the child to think about a favorite place in nature (e.g., the beach, the mountains, a favorite park, underwater).

2. Explore with the child all of the elements that might be in the favorite place, encouraging as many details as possible.

3. Move the child's bed to the window to paint the scene, or paint the scene on the window under the child's direction. Have the child direct all details (e.g., colors, size and placement of objects). If the child is able to leave the bed for even a limited period of time, he or she can paint special details or the finishing touches.

4. The child may tire of the "view" or want to change it with the seasons. Adding a few drops of dishwashing soap to the paint before applying will make it easier to remove.

Weaving On Fallen Tree Branches

Tree branch weaving can be a very quick and simple activity or something that a child works on over a period of time. A fallen tree branch or twig serves as a loom. In the hospital setting, a really large branch can be used for a group project to foster a sense of community and relieve feelings of isolation. The branch is taken from room to room, with each child weaving on a portion of the branch.

Materials

Fallen tree branches or twigs

Yarn (variegated yarn offers an easy method of changes in color)

Crewel embroidery needle

Process

1. Gather an interesting assortment of fallen tree branches and twigs, and ask the child to select one for use as a loom.
2. Have the child wrap yarn back and forth around ajacent pieces of the branch to form a warp.
3. Help the child threat the needle and demonstrate going over and under the warp to create the woof.
4. Encourage the child to experiement with different methods, such as skipping certain areas to create interesting openings.
5. Shells or other objects from nature can be incorporated into the design if desired.

SandCast Candles

This is a favorite activity for children who are hospitalized in the summertime. Simply take containers with moist sand and an old electric skillet filled with coffee cans with various colors of melted wax on a cart from room to room, plugging in the skillet occasionally to keep the wax liquid enough to pour. Because of infection control, we always use new sand (intended for sandboxes) found in home and garden stores. For children who are immunosuppressed, sand can be sterilized in an autoclave.

Materials

Sand

A container for the sand (wash basins work nicely)

Candle or canning wax (beeswax rather than petroleum based because of fumes)

Empty coffee cans (at least a couple to enable a choice of colors or mixing)

An old pan and source of heat

Crayons to add color

Water

White birthday candles

Oven mitts

Old metal spoons (ice tea size is good)

Newspaper

Process

1. Have the child put wax and desired color crayon in the coffee can.
2. Fill the old pan with a couple of inches of water, place the coffee

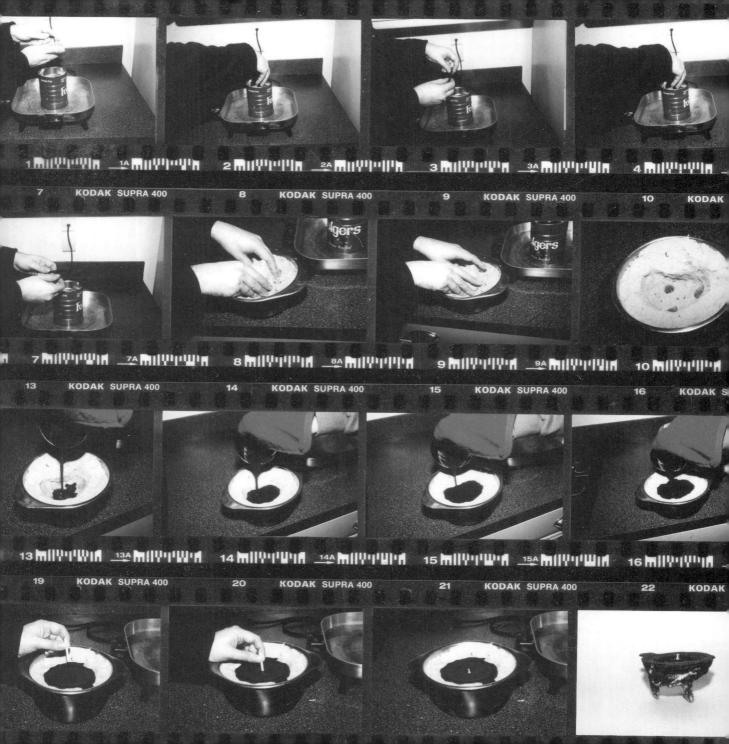

can in the pan, and heat it over low to medium heat until the wax has completely melted.

3. Moisten the sand with water until it holds a shape.

4. Have the child use hands or other tools to create a mold by forming a simple shape in the negative in the sand.

5. Stir wax with spoon if even distribution of color is desired.

6. Using the oven mitts, pick up the coffee can and pour the hot wax into the mold. For safety reasons, the artist usually performs this step.

7. Let the wax cool for about 5 minutes until it starts getting somewhat solid.

8. Have the child add a birthday candle to make a wick.

9. Spread out newspaper.

10. After the wax has completely cooled (anywhere from 20–90 minutes depending upon size), have the child remove the candle from the sand and shake the loose sand back into the container.

Side Walk

As soon as the weather turns warm, a familiar sight is children playing and creating art on sidewalks. With a bit of imagination, you can bring this same sense of fun to the child's bedside. How much of the project the child will be able to do alone will depend upon age and ability, but he or she can still make important choices and decisions about colors and other details and guide you in the execution.

Materials

Terra cloth or canvas
Scissors
Newspapers
Ruler or yardstick
Pencil
Acrylic paint—black, white, and other colors, if you like
Plastic, aluminum, or paper plate for mixing paint
Container with water
Masking tape (½" wide)
Sponges
Dustless chalk
Piece of soft cloth

Process

1. Cut a piece of terra cloth approximately 4" x 24" and place it on the newspaper.
2. Have the child mix the black and white paint together to create a sidewalk color grey. Other colors may be added if desired. It is okay if the color is not totally blended; it will have a more realistic appearance. Add water as needed to thin paint.
3. Have the child use sponges to apply the color to completely cover the terra cloth.

4. Once the paint is dry, mark off six 4" x 4" blocks with the ruler and pencil.

5. Using the masking tape, mask off an area approximately 1/8 on either side of the lines.

6. Dip a sponge in a darker shade of paint and instruct the child to cover the area between the pieces of tape to create sidewalk "cracks."

7. Once the paint is dry, ask the child to remove the masking tape.

8. Have the child create sidewalk art using the colored chalk. The soft cloth can be used to erase the images and start over again.

9. The completed sidewalk may be used in other ways as well:

- **Art piece**—The sidewalk drawing can be framed or attached to a dowel rod and displayed.

- **Hopscotch**—The child can draw a hopscotch game and make people out of clothespins to play hopscotch or other games. The peg people can be rolled up in the sidewalk, tied with string, and put away until the child is ready to play again.

- **Tic-tac-toe**—The sidewalk can be used to play tic-tac-toe with family members, friends, or the artist.

Leaf Prints on Fabric

Sometimes one of the most difficult things about being sick is having to stay inside on a lovely summer day. Creating a leaf print can bring the outdoors in, at least in a small way. And because a pounding activity is involved, the child has an opportunity to vent possible frustration and anger as well as to create a beautiful finished product.

We have used this process for wall hangings and tee shirts. This lends itself nicely to a group project, such as a table cloth (old sheets work great) or a large wall hanging. The fabric can be brought to the bedside so that all children can add their part. We once used this technique for families of persons with AIDS to create an altar cloth to be used at a retreat.

Materials

Freshly picked green leaves
Waxed paper
Smooth rock small enough for the child to handle
Cloth
Vinegar
Water
Bowl or other conatiner

Process

1. Have the child place leaves, vein side down, on a piece of waxed paper.
2. Cover the leaves with a piece of fabric.
3. Instruct the child to pound on the fabric with the rock. The juice from the leaves will start to appear and stain the fabric.
4. Have the child continue pounding

until the desired effect is obtained.

5. When finished, dip the fabric in vinegar solution (1 tablespoon of vinegar to 1 cup of water) to set dye. Hang to dry.

6. Glue to a piece of cardboard using rubber cement (away from the child) and frame or attach to a dowel for a wall hanging.

Note: Berries may be used in the same manner to add interest and color.

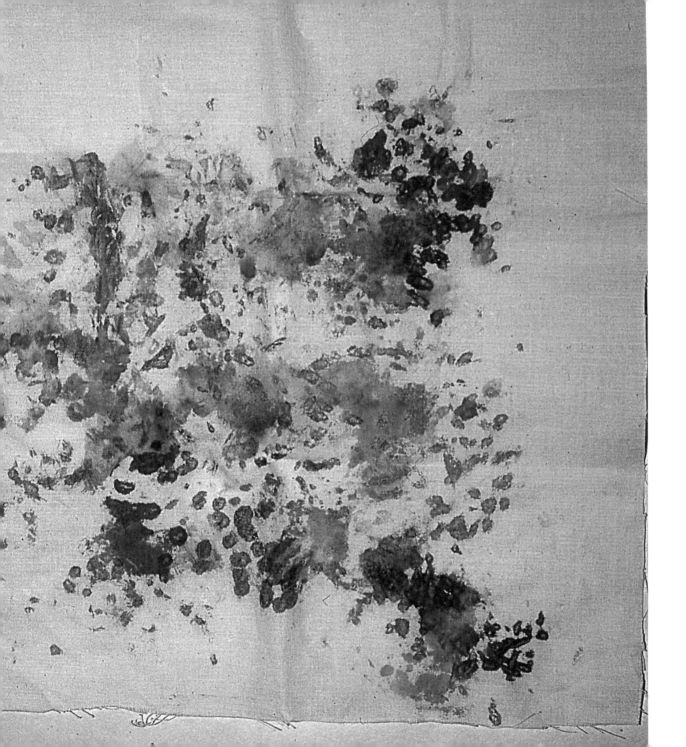

03 images

Joan Dresher

Details from Symbols of Courage Murals Number II: "Not Feeling Well"—Painted in the blue, cold color of fear and uncertainty, this mural depicts the feelings experienced upon receiving a diagnosis.

For a variety of reasons, visual arts activities often are favorite pastimes for children who are hospitalized or in bed at home. For example, with visual arts activities such as drawing, children can set their own pace, working for a time and putting it aside for awhile when they are tired. Also, in most instances, only simple materials are required and are readily available or easy to obtain. These simple materials and a child's imagination make a wonderful combination.

The activities in this section can be used with all ages of children. The nature of the activities lend themselves to being simplified for younger children or taken to a higher level by older children and adolescents.

Although the focus of this book is the participation of the child in arts activities, a discussion of images is incomplete without mentioning the impact of images in the healthcare environment upon children. Children who are sick, injured, or disabled are often more affected by their surroundings than their healthy peers (Olds & Daniel, 1987). Children, who live according to the information provided by their senses, remember places and sensations more than they remember people (Prescott & David, 1976). Thus, they likely are more sensitive to their surroundings than are adults, and may be affected deeply and for a long time by details of which adults are unaware.

Artist and children's author Joan Drescher's murals for healing environments reflect awareness of the power of images on children who are sick or hospitalized. In 1997, for example, she created a series of seven murals for the Children's Hematology/Oncology Clinic at the Floating Hospital for Children at New England Medical Center in Boston, MA. The series, entitled "Symbols of Courage," depicts the true-life stories of young patients who were undergoing treatment for cancer from diagnosis through the complete treatment protocol. Using proven theories of the value of visualization and positive imaging in the healing process, the symbols of hope empower children to tell their stories. Thus, the "art on the walls" also can be used as a stimulus for arts activities for children at bedside.

Drawing

Sometimes the most meaningful arts activities are simple ones, such as drawing. Drawing can be ongoing, providing the child with a means of communication, personal satisfaction, and pleasure. We give children sketchbooks. Children are more likely to save their drawings when they are together in one place. They can look back over time and reflect on their progress. A sketchbook can be written in as well, thus having the potential to serve as a journal. We like to give children professional hard cover sketchbooks; professional quality communicates respect for what will be inside.

Drawing can be approached from two angles—drawing from the imagination or recording visually what is being observed (Greaves, 1994). The first requires a wide range of built-in images to call upon; the second requires a different skill altogether, one that requires constant practice, just as writing and reading do. With older children, we often recommend the book *Drawing on the Right Side of the Brain* (Edwards, 1999) and for parents, *Child Art: A Parents' Handbook* (Greaves, 1994) to help develop this skill. We address both angles here.

Angle 1
Materials
Sketch book
Drawing
utensils
(pencils,
charcoal, crayons, oil pastels, felt tipped pens, aquarelles)
Handful of paper clips in a small plastic bag or other container

Process

1. Give the child a sketch book, explaining that it is his or hers to keep to draw and/or write in what ever and whenever he or she wishes.
2. Provide the child with a choice of drawing tools, demonstrating their special characteristics and use.
3. Give the child some paperclips.
4. Explain that if there is a time when the child does not want anyone to see a particular page, a paper clip can be used to clip the pages together until when, if ever, he or she is ready to share. In this way children are able to benefit from the catharsis of expression without fear that someone will see, judge, or analyze their thoughts, feelings, or fantasies (Rollins, in press).

Angle 2
Materials

Old magazines and newspapers with drawings of children, men, women, pets, other animals, transport (cars, ships, airplanes) buildings, trees, flowers, etc.
Scrapbook
Scissors
Glue, glue stick, or tape
Drawing tools (pencils, charcoal, crayons, oil pastels, felt tipped pens, aquarelles)
Paper

Process

1. Explain that one way to learn about drawing techniques is by looking at other people's drawings. Collecting examples of drawings from newspapers and magazines and saving them for references can be a beginning.
2. Give the child a stack of newspapers and magazines with instructions to find drawings of interest. This process can be ongoing.
3. Have or help the child cut out the drawings with the scissors.
4. Discuss the drawings with the child, looking at characteristics such as simplicity, complexity, bold or fine line, realistic or simplified.
5. Help the child to divide the images into categories (e.g., animals, buildings, people) and to glue or tape them into a scrapbook to serve as a resource of visual information when the child needs a symbol from a particular category.

6. When the child is ready to draw, present the sketchbook or paper and a variety of drawing tools, and demonstrate their special characteristics and use.

7. Try to encourage a greater diversity of symbols. While the child is drawing, ask questions about details. For instance, about an animal the child is drawing, you could ask the following questions:

- Where does your animal live? What does your animal's house look like?
- What does your animal like to eat?
- What does your animal do during the day? Go to school? Go to work? Play?
- Does your animal have brothers and sisters?

8. After the child has completed a drawing (children typically know when they are finished and often announce, "I'm done!"), encourage further diversity by asking the child to repeat the drawing, but this time trying to image another point of view. Ask questions such as the following:

- What would the figures look like from the side, back, from above, down on the ground, and so on?
- Can you make the figures bend, skip, jump, hop, etc?

9. Explain that drawings can be considered finished art or can serve as notes for more detailed productions.

Mandalas

Mandalas are personal symbols that reveal who we are at the moment. The circle contains—even invites—conflict in parts of our nature to appear. There is an undeniable release of tension when making a mandala, even when conflict surfaces. This may be because the form of the circle recalls the safe closeness of the womb (Fincher, 1991). Drawing a circle may be something like drawing a protective line around us. We create our own sacred space, a place of protection, a focus for the concentration of our energies. A sense of unity may be achieved merely from the act of drawing within the circle. Children may experience a reality of harmony, peace, and meaningfulness.

Mandalas are best created in solitude, with an attitude of reverence for the external patterns of the Self and respect for the truth of the moment. Although perhaps most appropriate for adolescents, we have found that children as young as 6 or 7 are capable of and enjoy making mandalas.

Materials
White or black drawing paper, 12" X 18"
Oil pastels, colored chalks,
markers, colored pencils, or paints
10-inch paper plate or other round object

Process
1. Place paper and drawing implements on a flat surface in a well-lit and quiet setting.
2. Have the child place the paper plate in the center of the paper and, using it as a guide, draw a circle on the paper.

3. Ask the child to begin, using as little thought as possible, to fill in the circle with color and form. The child can begin in the center or around the edge of the circle, with or without a pattern in mind; there is no right or wrong way to create a mandala.

4. Have the child continue to work until the mandala is complete.

5. When finished, ask the child to turn the drawing to identify the proper position of the mandala, disregarding the edges of the paper and looking only at the design itself. When the proper orientation is found, have the child mark the top of the mandala with a small "t."

6. Ask the child to date the mandala for future reference, including the month, day, and year.

7. Place the mandala "t" side up at least an arm's length distance away. Children often feel an ineffable satisfaction upon completing a mandala and the mandala meditation can end here. Others may want to concentrate on their mandalas by drinking in the forms and colors with their eyes to give themselves valuable visual feedback.

Note. Adapted from "Creating Mandalas for Insight, Healing, and Self-Expression" by S. Fincher, 1991, Boston: Shambhala. The book is an excellent resource for interpreting the colors, forms, and other symbols in the mandala.

Moment Boards

A few years ago we purchased an item for our program called a Zen Board. Children are fascinated with the board; they paint with water and the strokes turn a rich black immediately. The image lasts about 10 minutes. We talk about how important it is to savor the moment, because the image, as with many things in life—such as flowers—will not always be there. Children with life threatening conditions seem to connect and gain comfort from the concept of appreciating the moment.

Recently, Valerie Conzett, an artist in Omaha, Nebraska, uncovered and shared with us the secret of the magic boards. Now we help children make their own.

Materials

Rigid corrugated cardboard 11" X 14"
Precut mat 11" X 14" with a 7½" X 9½" opening
Brush-Up paper*
Scissors
Rubber cement
Bamboo brush
Container for water

Process

1. With the Brush Up paper right side up, put a dab of rubber cement on each corner.
2. Center the mat board over the Brush Up paper and press to adhere.
3. Turn over and apply more rubber cement in area backed by the mat board, being careful to avoid getting any on the Brush Up paper.

4. Press mat board (with attached Brush Up paper) to corrugated cardboard to form a solid bond.
5. Provide a container of water and bamboo brush and invite the child to make a brush stroke.
6. Explain that only clean water and a clean brush can be used on the board, and that oversaturation should be avoided. Let the water evaporate naturally.

*Available in many art supply stores or through Dick Blick (www.dickblick.com)

Note: For an alternative method, as shown here, simply remove the glass from a picture Frame and Frame Brush-Up Paper backed by rigid corrugated cardboard cut to size.

Marble Painting

The first time we used this activity was with a 9-month old baby with leukemia who had been in isolation for three weeks. He was spell bound as he watched the colors magically appear under his control. His mother seemed energized as she observed his delight. Sometimes we tend to forget that when a small child is isolated, often his or her parent is as well.

Marble painting is an activity that can be used with all ages of children, an activity that can be taken "up or down." At one level the child can simply tilt or shake the container and watch the colors appear. At a higher level the child can choose colors and move the container to paint with some degree of intent. Regardless of technique, there is always some element of surprise.

Materials
Small bowls
Tempera paints in a variety of colors
Plastic spoons
A flat container with a clear lid (note: those used at salad bars work nicely)
White and/or colored paper cut to fit into the bottom of the container
Scissors
Newspaper

Process

1. Pour a different color of paint into each bowl. You may want to leave at least one bowl empty so that the child can mix colors.
2. Have the child place a marble in each container.
3. Ask the child to choose a piece of paper and place the paper in the bottom of the container.
4. Ask the child to select a color, scoop up the marble coated with the color with a spoon, and place the marble on the paper in the container.
5. Close the container lid.
6. Have the child tilt or shake the marble around the container, making trails of paint on the paper.
7. When the child is satisfied with the results, remove the marble and replace with a marble from another color.
8. Continue until the child indicates that the painting is finished.
9. Remove painting and place on newspaper to dry.
10. Finished papers may be framed or cut and used in collages, as wrapping paper, or to make greeting or postcards. Children's individual work may be combined in a group piece.

Silkscreen Circle Prints

This technique is simple, quick, inexpensive, and produces exciting results. The circle design lends itself well to projects requiring a consistent theme. For example, a child can create a series of these circle prints on paper, or individual children can each complete a circle print on fabric, which are then sewn together to form a community wall hanging or quilt.

Materials

Nylon stocking or an organdy-like fabric
Embroidery hoop
Scissors
Heavy paper or card stock
Printer's ink (Use fabric ink for printing on fabric. To cut costs, thicken powered tempera paints to replace printer's ink when printing on paper.)
Paper or fabric
Small squeegee or piece of cardboard

Process

1. Stretch nylon stocking or an organdy-like fabric on an embroidery hoop.
2. Ask the child to cut out a shape from the card stock to use as a stencil. (Leaves may be used as stencils to bring the outdoors in.)
3. Have the child place the stencil on the fabric or paper.
4. Cover the stencil with the silkscreen hoop, stocking side down.
5. Place blobs of printer's ink in the circle.
6. Have the child distribute the ink throughout the entire circle using a small squeegee or piece of cardboard.
7. Carefully remove hoop and stencil and allow print to dry.
8. Wash screen with soap and water and let dry. (To speed drying, use a hairdryer.)

Bubble Paintings

The first time we tried this was on Halloween. We used a big black pot, which we called a witch's caldron. The bubbles make beautiful, one-of-a-kind designs. Children can use the paper as is as book covering, wrapping paper, book marks, or notepaper. Some children may want to use it as a background for drawing, painting, or collage.

Materials

Dishwashing liquid
Bowls, cups, or other containers
Drinking straws
Food coloring
Watercolor, construction paper, or any kind of thick paper with "tooth"
Paintbrushes

Process

1. Ask the child to squeeze about ½" of dishwashing liquid into the bottom of the bowl. The child will need one bowl for each color desired.
2. Add several squirts of food coloring into each bowl and mix with a paintbrush.
3. Once the paint is well mixed, have the child add a few drops of water into the mixture.
4. Ask the child to take the straw and blow into the mixture, continuing until the bubbles reach the top of the bowl. More water may be needed if the child has difficulty getting the mixture to bubble.

5. Have the child place a piece of paper over the bowl for a few seconds and then lift up. Beautiful bubble patterns will appear. More than one color can be used on the same paper.
6. Suggest ways that the paper can be used, or provide the child with additional art materials for drawing, painting, collage, etc.

Note: The paper makes a lovely cover for a special book or journal.

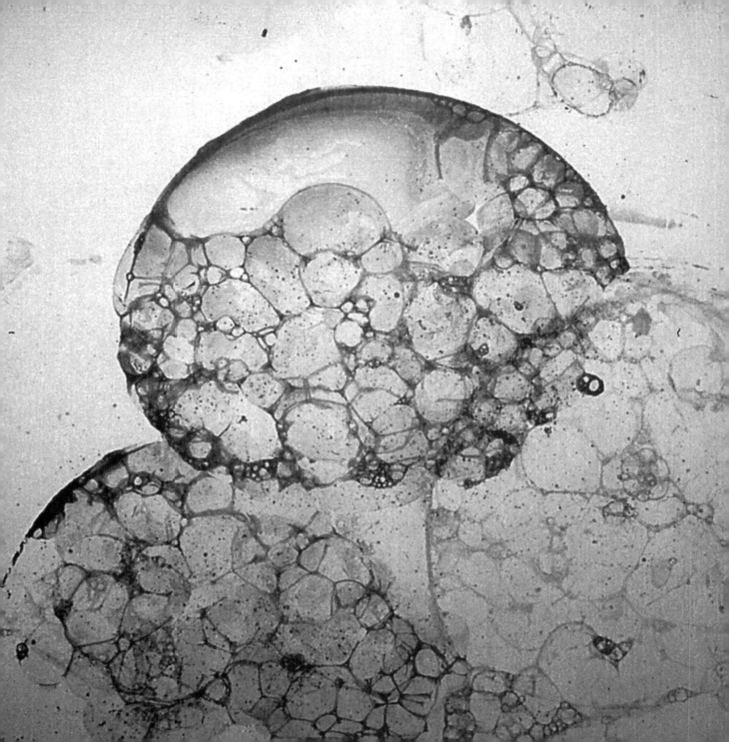

Life Necklace

The Life Necklace is a beadmaking project begun by Lacretia Johnson as a response to the fears and developmental issues that children face while in the hospital. Children and their family members make beads for the Life Necklace and Lacretia keeps a written record of the story behind each unique bead. Through the sharing of the stories, the Life Necklace has become a vehicle that fosters a sense of community that extends across generations, ethnicities, cultural and socio-economic backgrounds, and types of illness and injury (Johnson, 1997).

This activity can be facilitated easily in hospital settings by going room to room with a toaster oven on a cart, with oven set up in well ventilated area. And even though most homes have ovens, Lacretia always brings along her toaster oven when making home visits because the family oven may be unavailable.

Materials

Polymer clay in different colors
Plastic knife
Oven, regular or toaster oven (Do not use a microwave oven.)
Cookie sheet covered with aluminum foil
Coffee stirrers
Ribbon or cord
Toothpick
Potholders

Process

1. Cut blocks of clay into smaller pieces.
2. Ask child to select the colors he or she wants to use.
3. Demonstrate how new colors can be created through mixing.
4. Demonstrate how to shape beads by rolling them with your hands or on the table. Point out that beads do not need to be round. For an excellent resource on beadmaking techniques, see *The New Clay: Techniques and Approaches to Jewelry Making* by Nan Roche (1991).
5. Explain that toothpicks can be used on the beads to create texture or carve words or images.
6. Before baking the beads, use a coffee stirrer to make a hole that goes all the way through the bead.
7. Place beads on cookie sheet and bake in a 275° oven, 10 minutes for small beads, 15 minutes for larger ones. Use a well-ventilated area.
8. Remove from oven and allow beads to cool.
9. For individual necklaces, cut a piece of ribbon or cord that is long enough to go over the child's head. For a Life Necklace, add beads to a long piece of ribbon or cord and tie a knot on either side of the beads to prevent sliding.
10. Wash hands (yours and the child's) after using the clay.

Personal Containers

A child's illness or disability can tend to dominate the child's life and identity. Yet, underneath the illness or disability is foremost a child, a child with many other equally important characteristics. This activity allows children to reflect on and express who they are, and works especially well with teenagers who under even normal circumstances are struggling with identity issues.

Creating an object that represents self provides a powerful mechanism for getting to know the whole child. With knowledge comes the trust necessary to form a connected relationship—the kind that we encourage our artists to establish—in which the child is viewed first as a person and second as a patient.

Artists may want to work alongside children and create their own personal containers as a means of helping children get to know them.

Materials
Paper
Pencil
Remainder to be detemined by the child upon consultation with the artist

Process

1. Explain that you would like to help the child design and construct a container that represents his or her personal interests. Give some examples of containers—objects that can hold things, e.g., boxes, vases, purses, bowls, pillow cases.

2. Ask the child to think about and list all of the things that are of personal interest, all of the things that make the child who he or she is.

3. Help the child draw plans for the container. Although some children may want to use an existing box or other container, others may want to start from scratch. In some cases the child may need to make a small "maquette" (trial model) first to ensure that the design will work.

4. Assemble the materials the child needs to make the container. Have the child consider how to treat the inside as well as the outside surfaces when deciding on materials, e.g., paint, collage, relief.

5. Bring closure to the project by encouraging the child to include carefully selected items in the container that represent different facets of self.

Words
Words
Word
04 Words

Words, written or spoken, provide real coping tools for children who are ill or hospitalized. Particularly for children with chronic, disabling, or life threatening conditions, the ability to draw upon the creative spirit can help maintain a sense of hopefulness, provide an outlet for the expression of feelings, and open the door to an exciting world of possibilities.

In describing how writing can help children facing serious illness, Dion (2000) mentions several benefits. Writing improves the spirits. Although Dion does not claim that a positive spirit developed through writing can cure someone, she does believe that it will aid individuals in numerous ways, and for some, it will enhance the road to recovery.

Writing provides escape. Children can travel to distant lands or return to previously enjoyed experiences through their imaginations. Writing provides a platform for children to express their anger, sadness, grief, happiness, joy, and other emotions.

Writing, particularly journaling, provides a method for children to measure, monitor, and celebrate their progress. For example, often tucked away inside is the extent of impact of a profound experience, such as being told a poor prognosis or undergoing a difficult procedure. However, looking back to an earlier journal entry provides a visible and authentic record and the opportunity for children to truly acknowledge what they have been through, integrate it into their life experience, and move forward.

Children can be introduced to the joy of "words" in many ways. Providing simple materials—paper and pen or pencil—or a laptop computer, will encourage children to write. Children also can be invited to visit words through the all time favorite wordsmith—the storyteller.

Getting Started

Writing is one way for children's voices to be heard—or not heard, if they choose not to share. Either way, children benefit from the process. Below, we have adapted two methods offered by Susan Dion, author of *Write Now: Maintaining a Creative Spirit While Homebound and Ill (2000)* that children who are ill or hospitalized seem to enjoy.

What Should I Write?
Materials
Paper and pen or pencil, or
A laptop computer

Process
1. Invite the child to "move to a special place" to write. He or she many change position in bed or simply move to a different place through the imagination.

2. Provide writing materials and offer some suggestions for things to write about:
   - A window and the view from it
   - A room, the different parts of it, one or more of the things in it, the smells, sounds, connections, colors
   - Wallpaper patterns or the patterns found in ceiling, tile, floor, walls, clothing, towel, sheets, bedspread, rugs
   - People, one person or a group (e.g., doctors—real doctors, TV and film doctors, good or bad doctors, doctor stories, the perfect doctor)
   - Animals, fish, birds, insects, pets
   - Small items, a box, a bottle of lotion, a bowl of soup, a fork, a sandal, a fallen twig, a bedpost

3. Have child develop "Top 10 lists" to write about:
- Top 10 things that make the child laugh, chuckle, or smile
- Top 10 most satisfying experiences
- Top 10 major struggles overcome
- Top 10 people in the news who really get on the child's nerves, and why
- Top 10 quirky people the child knows
- Top 10 favorite films, books, foods, cars, locations, people, TV programs, musical compositions (and why)
- Top 10 fluffy, silly, fun fantasies
- Top 10 elements of an ideal community
- Top 10 petty daily annoyances
- Top 10 of the absolutely worst points about living with his or her illness
4. Help the child who enjoys writing schedule a time for writing each day.

Journaling
Materials
Any kind of notebook or journal
Pen or pencil

Process
1. Present the child with pencils, pens, and a variety of blank books from which to choose. Many children prefer sketchbooks, which allow them to draw as well as write journal entries.
2. Explain the difference between a diary and a journal: diaries are typically daily records of one's experiences, while journals are often considered a place for reflection, commentary, and soul-searching.
3. Point out that journals can be used to problem solve. Seeing one's thoughts on a problem can clarify issues and lead to solutions.
4. Provide the child with suggestions for journaling:
- Reflections on being sick, disabled, or limited
- Self talk (e.g., "I will...I will not")
- Exploration of a social or world problem
- Powerful emotions
5. Help the child who enjoys this activity schedule a time each day for journaling.

*Note: The book, *Write Now*, is a non-profit resource supported by donations and grants, and is distributed free on-line (http://home.main.rr.com/painsupport/writenow/).

Poetry

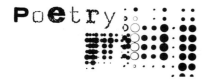

Poetry, the most compressed form of literature, is composed of carefully chosen words that may express great depth of meaning or simply be fun. Children can explore writing various types of poems—Rhyming couplet, Quatrain, Limerick, Chiquan, Haiku, Shape poem, Free-form. Poetry also can take visual form through creative methods of display.

The poetry activities below are simple and designed to be used with children with low energy levels. The visiting poet serves as the scribe.

Name Poems
Materials
Paper and pen or pencil, or
A laptop computer

Process
1. Write the child's name vertically on a piece of paper or type it vertically on a laptop computer. For example, if the child's name is Juan:

   J
   U
   A
   N

2. Ask the child to think of a word or phrase that describes how he or she is feeling right now that begins with each letter. For example,

   Jerked around
   Under the weather
   Angry
   Nauseated

3. Ask the child if he or she would like to talk about the responses and expand on the poem. Discussion can center around problem solving when negative feelings are shared.

A Silliness Group Poem
Materials
Same as above

Process
1. Ask the child to supply the missing words: *I am like a* _____ *because I can* _____ Provide an example: *I am like an octopus because I can do many things at the same time*. Record the child's response.
2. Follow by asking the child to supply the missing words: *I looked at a* __ *and out* _____ . Provide an example: *I looked at a balloon and out popped a magician*. Record the child's response.
3. End with a third request for words: *I opened up* _____ *and out* _____ . Provide an example: *I opened up*

the refrigerator and out rolled a rooster. Record the child's response.
4. Ask others (family members, friends, or if hospitalized, roommates and others on the ward) for their responses and record.
5. Record everyone's responses and then return to read the completed poem to each child.

What If Poems
Materials
Same as above

Process
1. Ask the child to consider one of the following "What ifs" for a theme for a poem:
- If I were older
- If I could go back in time
- If I could go forward in time
- If I were a doctor (or nurse) for the day
- If I could be anywhere else right now
- If I could meet any movie star (sport figure)
- If I could be anyone in history
- If I won the lottery

2. Assist the child in developing a poem about the chosen theme by asking for as many details as possible.
3. Record the child's responses.

Displaying Poetry

1. Lines of poetry can be written and numbered on separate pieces of paper and displayed in various places in the child's room or on the hospital ward.
2. Poetry can be written with fabric pens on quilts and other wall hangings.
3. Poet Adele Steiner invented "Sky-writing" for a young girl in the terminal stages of cancer. Due to fatigue, the child was spending increasing amounts of time in bed. The child had only to look to the "sky" to read the beautiful poem she created that Adele posted on the ceiling above her bed. When the child died, we took a photo of the skywriting, typed out the entire poem in a beautiful script, matted and framed the two together, and presented it to the family at the child's memorial service.

storytelling

"I tell stories on pediatric wards because stories entertain; they distract children from their pain and worry," says Susan Gordon, Storyteller. "It gives them a chance to play, to create, to imagine, to have sustained human contact, to have choice, to speak, to ask for what they want, to express themselves, to have the time enough to say what is really on their minds, to ask questions, to get the story they really need."

Intense moments in our lives cry out for human contact. Simply offering a storybook to a child may be helpful, but research tells us that directed activities are more effective (Banks, Davis, Howard, & McLaughlin, 1993). This makes sense, for interactions among people are the foundations of any therapeutic or healing activity (The Pew-Fetzer Task Force, 1995).

With storytelling, the storyteller's presence is critical; a close caring communication is implicit in the storytelling relationship.

Storytellers for Children at Bedside

1. People become storytellers for a variety of reasons. There is some element of the "performer" in every storyteller; however performing cannot be the primary focus for the storyteller at bedside. There must be equal willingness to "take in" as well as to "give out." Together the storyteller and child agree to a mutual performance, as sometimes fun, sometimes scary, but a revered dance of "give and take."

2. To be able to take what the child has to offer, the storyteller must be an open vessel ready to receive, respect, and safeguard the always precious but sometimes raw offering from the child. He or she must be able to accept these offerings on the spot, often not understanding at the time what they mean, but able to move forward with the knowledge that these offering are real and therefore must be true and treated with the dignity that all human offerings deserve.

3. The successful storyteller at bedside is patient and willing to let the child lead the way.

4. Storytellers need to be acutely aware of how a child is responding along the way.

General Thoughts About Storytelling

1. Children who are coping with illness, hospitalization, injury, or dying often have powerful stories to tell. Professional storytellers as members of a child's healthcare team can make the most of the compelling need we all have to make sense of and attach meaning to what we are experiencing.

2. Storytellers can offer children stories that can truly help them to deal with both mental and physical pain. The power of story to distract should not be taken lightly. In 1794, before the use of anesthetics, a young boy had surgery to remove a tumor. He was told such an interesting story during his operation that it absorbed his attention and removed pain from conscious awareness. Eighteen years later, this true believer in the power of story, Jacob Grimm, wrote *Snow White* (Hilgard & LeBaron, 1984).

3. Stories can be used as guided imagery to help children relax.

4. Stories make it easier for children to deal with fears and realities by doing so indirectly. Fantasy skills can be used as tools for coping, even when the situation is grave.

5. Children take from a story only what they are ready to find. A well-chosen story permits children to discuss their issues and situations if they wish; other children simply enjoy a story as a fantasy escape that need not be analyzed.

6. Simply asking children to share recollections of home and school experiences can decrease their sense of isolation.

7. Having children speak their stories into a microphone for a "radio show" and audio-taping their stories brings additional dimensions.

8. Rhythm and music, chants and songs make exciting additions to storytelling.

9. The structure of stories——a beginning, middle, and end——within a definite timeframe, offers a sense of predictability to children at a time in their lives when many things may be unpredictable.

Suggested Stories and Resources

Familiar stories, such as *Goldilocks and the Three Bears*, *Three Little Pigs*, and *Billy Goats Gruff*, are wonderful to use at bedside. Hearing something familiar and predictable can provide children with a sense of comfort and safety.

Many appropriate and excellent stories can be found in the following publications:

Cole, J. (1992). *Best-loved folktales of the world*. New York: Doubleday.

Defty, J. (1992). *Creative fingerplays and action rhymes for toddlers: An index and guide to their use.* Phoenix, AZ: Oryx.

Forest, H. (1995). *Wonder tales from around the world.* Little Rock, AR: August House.

Holt, D., & Mooney, B. (1994). *Ready-to-tell tales: Sure-fire stories from America's favorite storytellers.* Little Rock, AR: August House.

MacDonald, M. (1995). *The parent's guide to storytelling: How to make up new stories and retell old favorites.* New York: HarperCollins.

Pellowski, A. (1984). *The story vine: A source book for unusual and easy-to-tell stories from around the world.* New York: Macmillan.

The following publications provide helpful information about storytelling with children in healthcare settings:

Bettelheim, B. (1976). *The uses of enchantment: The meaning and importance of fairy tales.* New York: Knopf.

Coen, J. (1996). The use of fairytales as therapy with traumatised children. *Children in Hospital, 22* (1), 12–13.

Freeman, M. (1991). Therapeutic use of storytelling for older children who are critically ill. *Children's Health Care, 20* (4), 208–215.

Glendon, K., & Dreyer, L. (1993). Using a personal storybook and Mr. Potato Head® toy as a creative approach to individualized teaching. *The ACCH Advocate, 1* (1), 49–51.

Heiney, S. (1995). The healing power of story. *Oncology Nursing Forum, 22* (6), 899–904.

Hudson, C., Leeper, J., Strickland, M., & Jesse, P. (1987). Storytelling: A measure of anxiety in hospitalized children. *Children's Health Care, 16* (2), 118–122.

Kuttner, L. (1988). Favorite stories: A hypnotic pain-reduction technique for children in acute pain. *American Journal of Clinical Hypnosis, 30* (4), 289–295.

Neill, C. (1993). Storymaking and storytelling: Weaving the fabric that creates our lives. In B. Warren (Ed.), *Using the creative arts in therapy* (2nd ed.) (pp. 133–160). London: Routledge.

05 Sounds

Sounds have a powerful influence on children who are ill. Particularly for children who are hospitalized, sounds can be frightening—such as hearing the crying of another child and wondering if what is happening to that child "will also happen to me." However, sounds within hospitals also can be calming—such as the soft notes from a visiting harpist or the gentle voice of a parent or nurse singing a lullaby.

Music has the broadest reach of any of the arts used at bedside. There are many ways that the child can be actively involved, such as singing or playing a musical instrument. Music can be used with individuals of any age under almost any circumstances. Even babies respond to music. In our work in hospitals, we have watched monitors in amazement as oxygen saturation rates rise when a musician strums a soothing melody on the guitar and sings quietly to a child. Also, because research tells us that hearing is still present when an individual is comatose, even the child who is unconscious or dying is believed to benefit from hearing music. Certain kinds of music can be used to engage and support life processes, while other kinds can be used to help the child who is dying move toward completion and to unbind from anything that prevents, impedes, or clouds a tranquil passage. A new music field—music thanatology—has emerged to address the complex needs of people who are dying. To learn more about the effects of different types of music, see McCraty, Barrios-Choplin, Atkinson, and Tomasino (1998) and Schroeder-Sheker (1993).

Another advantage of music is that others in the child's environment can also enjoy listening or even participating in the activity. In the home care setting, participants can include family and friends; in the hospital or hospice setting, nurses, doctors, and other hospital personnel have the same options. Therefore, music has significant implications for caring for the caregiver as well as the "identified patient."

MuSical Instruments

Many musical instruments can be made using very simple supplies and methods. Below are a few suggestions. Some ideas may be new to you, but others will likely be familiar old favorites. We usually demonstrate by making our own instrument, helping the child to follow along.

Poppers
Materials
A 50cc syringe

Process
1. Ask the child if he or she would like to hear a syringe make music.
2. If the answer is yes, demonstrate the popping sound made when the plunger is moved in and out.
2. Invite the child to try, remembering that some children may be fearful of the syringe from its association with needles, and refuse.

Harp
Materials
A small Y-shaped branch
2–4 rubber bands

Process
1. Stretch the rubber bands from one branch of the Y to the other.
2. Demonstrate how to play the harp by plucking the rubber bands with your fingers.

Kazoo
Materials
Small comb
Waxed paper

Process
1. Wrap a comb in waxed paper.
2. Put one end to your mouth and blow.

Maracas

Use caution when working with small children on this project because (a) balloons are an inhalation and choking hazard, and (b) small children may try to put objects such as dried beans in their ears, nose, or mouth.

Materials

Balloons
Stick or dowel about 4" in length
Masking or adhesive tape
Dried beans, unpopped popcorn, or rice
Plaster impregnated gauze
Scissors
Needle or pin
Acrylic paint
Paint brush
Bowl with water

Process

1. Place a handful of dried beans, unpopped popcorn, or rice into a balloon.
2. Blow up the balloon and tie a knot at the end.
3. Secure the balloon to the end of the the stick with tape.
4. Cut strips of plaster gauze into manageable lengths (about 3"–4")
5. Dip strips in water and apply to taped area.
6. Continue applying a few layers of gauze until the entire balloon and stick are covered.
7. Let dry completely, which, depending upon the number of layers, could take about 45 minutes to several hours.
8. Once dry, insert a needle or pin to pop the balloon.
9. Paint the instrument and let dry.
10. Demonstrate the sound by shaking.

Jar Xylophone
Materials

Baby food jars or glasses
(8 is a good number)
Water
Metal spoon

Process

1. Fill jars with increasing amounts of water.
2. Gently strike the side of each jar with the spoon, pointing out the difference in sound.
3. Demonstrate how the various sounds can be used to create a tune.

Rainstick

Many methods can be used to make rainsticks. We like this one because it is simple and quick, and it does not involve nails that tend to work their way out of the tube.

Materials

Cardboard packing tube
Heavy duty aluminum foil
Dried beans, unpopped popcorn or rice
Adhesive or masking tape
Tissue paper
Glue
Acrylic paint
Feathers, beads, string, ribbon
Brushes
Water

Process

1. Tear off a 6" piece of aluminum foil and roll it into a strip.
2. Spiral the strip and place it inside the packing tube so that it runs from top to bottom. For a large tube, you may need to use more than one strip.
3. Fill the tube with a cup of dried beans, unpopped popcorn, rice, or a mixture.
4. Cover the end of the tube, and tape both ends securely.
5. Using glue, apply tissue paper to entire surface.
6. When dry, paint and finish with other decorative objects as desired.

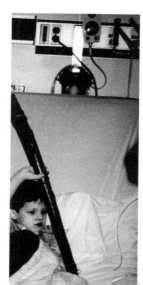

We give thanks for singers.

All types of singers.

Popular, concert singers and tuneless singers in the bath.

Whistlers, hummers and those who sing while they work.

Singers of lullabies; singers of nonsense and small scraps of melody.

Singers on branches and rooftops.

Morning yodellers and evening warblers.

Singers in seedy nightclubs, singers in the street;

Singers in cathedrals, school halls, grandstands, back yards, paddocks, bedrooms, corridors, stairwells and places of echo and resonance.

We give praise to all those who give some small voice

To the everyday joy of the soul.

From "The Prayer Tree" by Michael Leunig, 1991

singing

Singing requires nothing more than a desire "to give some small voice to the everyday joy of the soul." Formal sessions led by a visiting musician can be the highlight of a child's day. However, parents, nurses, and other caregivers can include songs with everyday activities, such as bathing and eating (see 09 Going Through the Day).

Group Singing

One of the goals of any arts activity at bedside is to offer the child the opportunity to be involved to the greatest extent to which his or her condition permits. Below is the process one of our musicians has used successfully in hospital settings for many years.

Materials

A variety of percussion instruments (A multicultural assortment with instruments that may be new to children can be very exciting.)
Optional: A guitar or other portable instrument; an audiotape recorder and audiotapes

Process

1. Determine which children can be brought to a common area (e.g., playroom, activity room, hospital lobby). In the hospital setting, bringing a group of children together adds the important element of socialization. Children often can be brought in their beds to join a group music activity.
2. Invite everyone (e.g., passerby, family members, health care professionals) to join in.
3. Ask for suggestions for songs, "What kind of music do you like?"

4. Demonstrate the use of each percussion instrument and pass them to various participants to try.
5. Begin by leading the group in song. As children become more comfortable, encourage them to lead. You may want to try some melody merges (see "Songs That Go Together").
6. From time to time, ask participants to swap instruments.
7. If possible, tape the session and have copies made to distribute to each participant.

Song That Go Together

Certain songs, when sung or hummed all at the same time, sound beautiful together. Defloria Lane introduced us to this possibility using "Swing Low, Sweet Chariot," "When the Saints Go Marching In," and "Mamma Don't Allow No Guitar Playing in Here." A large group is not really needed for this activity. It still can be effective at the child's bedside with only two or three people singing.

Materials

Voices

Process

1. Divide the group into thirds.
2. Agree on three songs to sing from the following list:
- "Swing Low, Sweet Chariot"
- "When the Saints Go Marching In"
- "Goodnight, Ladies"
- "Amazing Grace"
- "She'll be Coming 'Round the Mountain"
- "The Crawdad Song" (You get a line, I'll get a pole, honey)
- "Mama Don't Allow No Guitar Pickin' in Here"
- "Are You Sleeping?"
- "Down by the Station"
- "White Coral Bells"
- "Row, Row, Row Your Boat"
- "Three Blind Mice"
- "Merrily We Roll Along"
3. Ask the first group to sing a selected song.
4. After they have finished one verse, ask them to repeat the song and have the second group begin with a different song.
5. When the first two groups are ready to repeat their songs, have the third group join in with a different song.
6. Repeat all together at least one more time.

wind chimes

A variety of items make good sounds when the wind blows. Children can use existing objects, such as spoons or seashells, or create their own pieces from clay. Regardless of the items used, we favor using clear fishing line to suspend the "chimes," although any string or yarn may be used. Some children like to suspend their wind chimes from their IV poles.

Below is one of our favorite wind chime methods using clay. Clay that can be fired makes the best sound; however, self-drying clay or polymer clay that can be baked in a toaster oven will work, too.

Materials

Clay
Rolling pin, bottle, or can
Knife
Plastic soda straw
Found objects, e.g., jewelry, keys
Toothpick
Fishing line
Scissors
Small piece of fallen tree branch or wooden dowel

Process

1. Have the child use a rolling pin, bottle, or can to roll out clay into slabs approximately ¼" thick.
2. Help the child cut rectangular or other shaped pieces of different sizes.
3. Using the soda straw, ask the child to punch a hole at one end of each piece.

4. Present an assortment of found objects (e.g., keys, old jewelry) and the toothpick to the child with instructions to press gently to create a design or to write or draw in the clay.
5. Depending upon the type of clay, fire, bake, or let dry.
6. Help the child cut fishing line of varying lengths for the number of clay pieces and help attach a piece of line through the hole in each piece and knot.
7. Instruct the child to attach each clay piece to the branch or dowel and attach another piece to serve as a hanger.
8. Hang the wind chime wherever the child desires.

06 Movement

Particularly for the kinesthetic child, a dancer is one of the greatest assets an art program can offer. Music usually accompanies the experience, bringing in the benefits from this powerful medium as well.

Children move to the limits of their capabilities. They often are quite surprised at how good they feel afterwards. Family, friends, and hospital staff can participate as well, bringing them similar benefits while adding the dimension of socialization for the child.

Although at first it may seem that few children who are hospitalized will be able to participate in dance or movement, a better understanding of dance/movement at bedside indicates the opposite. The activities in this section intend to increase this understanding while opening the reader's mind to the enormous potential of this exciting medium.

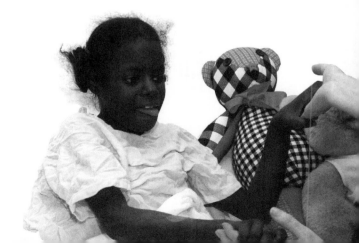

Movement Conversation

This activity, developed by Krissie Marty, is a conversation in movement. It provides an excellent opportunity for physical play and non-verbal communication in a very playful way. A physical dialogue is a fun way to relate and stretch movement range. Movement can happen standing, sitting, or lying down. Dances can be made with a movement range from eye blinks and nose wiggles to full-bodied jumping and falling and everything in between.

Materials
CD player
CDs

Process
1. Talk through the process with the child: "We will make a dance like a conversation. First, I will move and then become completely still and frozen. When I finish, then you will move."
2. Have the child choose a song or music to play in the CD player. Play the music. You can ask children to choose something from their own collection or have them choose a track off one of your CDs.
3. Position your body face-to-face with the child.
4. Have the child choose a starting position with some body parts touching, so the two of you are physically connected (e.g., palms facing, fingertips touching, elbows or feet together).
5. Move your body (3–5 seconds) and then freeze into complete stillness. Keep your frozen shape while the child moves, so you can "listen to what the child's body is saying."

6. Ask the child to make a movement of any kind and then freeze his or her complete stillness.

7. Respond to the child's movement with your own, then freeze into complete stillness.

8. Repeat this sequence —A move + freeze; B move + freeze.

9. Once the basic physical conversation is established, begin to change the speed and dynamic of the movement. You may also want to have longer "movement sentences."

10. If you need movement ideas, make 3-D doodles in the air. If a child doesn't know what to do for a movement, give a few choices (e.g., "Move your eyes in a circle or you can wiggle your fingers really slowly or you can shake your legs.")

11. Notice the child's movement intention and support it with your own movement.

12. Reinforce the child's movement intentions by continuing, repeating, developing, and playing with his or her movements.

Reach your arms higher or wider, closer or farther away. Articulate joints more fully, go slower or faster. Stop the movement and then start it again.

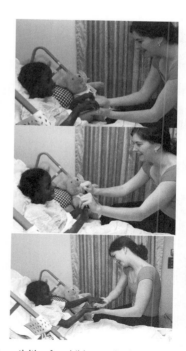

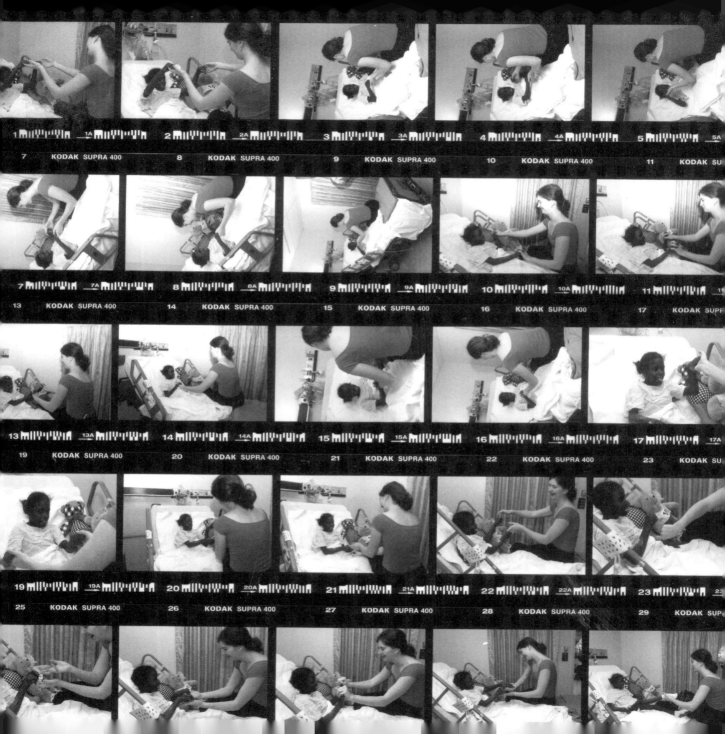

Mirroring

Krissie Marty uses this activity to explore a child's range of motion. It provides an opportunity for non-verbal expression and communication. There are often powerful and meaningful connections made in this movement exchange. It is also a chance to support the child's choices physically and verbally.

Again, movement can happen standing, sitting, or lying down. Dances can be made with a movement ranging from eye blinks and nose wiggles to full-bodied jumping and falling and everything in between.

Materials
CD player
CDs

Process

1. Talk through the process with the child: "We will dance together. We will make a mirror. I will do what you do for a while and then you will do what I do. Sometimes we will work together to make the same motion."

2. Have the child choose a song or music to play in the CD player. You can ask children to choose something from their own collection or have them choose a track off one of your CDs. For the first selection, use something with a slow tempo. A slower tempo in the music will encourage smooth and fluid movement, which allows for visible success in mirroring effect.

3. Play the music.

4. Position your body face-to-face with the child.

5. Ask if the child would like to begin as the leader.

6. Mirror the child's movement. Child leads: Follow and imitate exactly the child's movement. Notice the speed, direction, spatial range and dynamic range. Copy this as exactly as possible. Give the child verbal feedback and reinforcement: "I see you are moving your fingers with such small and tiny movements." Or "Your hands are moving so slow and steady from side to side, it makes it easy for me to follow you. " "That movement was so quick, you lost me. Can we try it again?"

7. Adult leads: If the child selects you as the leader, begin your movements slowly and in a small range while responding to the music. Allow the child to follow. Give verbal commentary if necessary: "I am reaching my hands slowly up, up, up."

8. Switch leaders. Child leads then adult leads (or the opposite) and continue switching. Give time for each leader to explore different movement ideas. After each full turn (child leads; adult leads), use less leading time, so that the duration between each switch is less and less. You and your partner may even begin switching without verbal communication!

9. Notice the child's movement intention and support it with your own movement. Reinforce the child's movement intentions by continuing, repeating, developing, and playing with the movements. Reach your arms higher or wider, closer or farther away. Articulate joints more fully, go slower or faster. Stop the movement and then start it again.

10. Use music with a faster tempo when you have established unified timing and a strong connection.

11. Play and have fun!

In the Ring

In the Ring is a children's dance from Jamaica. Yes, children in bed can participate in "group" dances. Any number of people will do, but a group of five or six individuals—family, friends, staff, other children—is ideal.

Materials
People

Process
1. Gather a group of individuals around the child's bed.
2. Explain the dance to the child and other participants.

This is a dance children do in Jamaica. It has four parts. One person is chosen to be "in the ring" and we sing the first part.

There's a young girl (boy) in the ring
Tra la la la la
A young girl (boy) in the ring
Tra la la la la
There's a young girl (boy) in the ring
Tra la la la la
For she (he) likes sugar and
I like plum

Next, the person in the ring "shows us a motion" while we sing the second part. Motions can be small, such a wiggling a finger or toe, or broad, such as waving the arms (demonstrate a few motions).

Then you show me a motion
Tra la la la la
You show me a motion
Tra la la la la
Then you show me a motion
Tra la la la la
For she (he) likes sugar and
I like plum

Then the person in the ring "swims across the ocean" (demonstrate a swimming movement with your arms) while we sing the third part.

> Then you swim across the ocean
> Tra la la la la
> Swim across the ocean
> Tra la la la la
> Then you swim across the ocean
> Tra la la la la
> For she (he) likes sugar and
> I like plum

During the fourth part, the person in the ring chooses a partner and points to that individual to be the next person in the ring, and the dance begins again.

> Then you stand and face your partner
> Tra la la la la
> Stand and face your partner
> Tra la la la la
> Then you stand and face your partner
> Tra la la la la
> For she (he) likes sugar and
> I like plum

3. Continue around the bed until every one has had a turn.

Note: This activity is fun to do one-on-one with babies, moving their arms or legs for the motions while singing.

Shadow Drama

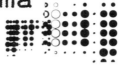

The hand shadow is a simple method of bringing drama to children at bedside. All that is needed are hands, a source of light, and a plain surface (e.g., a wall) to cast shadows upon. The first shadow drama was probably performed by candlelight, which might be interesting to try if safety regulations permit. Bright sunlight shining through a window may also be an option.

Materials
Source of light (flashlight, sunlight, lamp)
Optional: music

Process
1. Before visiting the child, practice positioning your hands in various ways to create shadows that resemble different animals. Rabbits and dogs are typically easy to learn. Choose a story with the animals for some ideas.
2. Position yourself at the child's bedside near the source of light and introduce the "characters" to the child.
3. Tell a simple story using the characters.
4. Teach the child how to create characters and have the child create a "play" or create one together. The addition of music can add another element to the drama.
5. If the child shows interest, move on to some more sophisticated hand shadows. An excellent resource is *Hand Shadows* by Henry Bursill (1993).

Note: The Shadow Drama may be videotaped.

Puppet Drama

Most younger school aged children love to create puppet shows. Although there are many methods for making elaborate puppets, with a sick child's limited energy, sometimes simple is best. These three simple puppets also provide an excellent way to introduce yourself, communicate, and establish rapport with a young child. Two of the puppets use medical supplies, lending this activity as a way to introduce medical play.

Storytellers at bedside often like to include an activity that involves the creation of a leave behind product. Children can make these puppets to accompany the story, or make them after the telling to accompany their own versions of the story.

Gauze Puppets
Materials
Gauze (a 4" X 4" works well)
Rubber band
Pen or colored marker

Process
1. Cover your index and middle fingers with a piece of gauze.
2. Secure with a rubber band
3. Make facial features with the pen or colored marker.
4. Have your puppet introduce him or herself and introduce you to the child.

Finger/Leg Puppets
Materials
3" X 5" unlined index cards or similar size card stock
Scissors
Colored markers

Process

1. Make one or two puppets ahead of time to show to the child as an example. Insert two fingers in the leg holes and demonstrate how the puppet is used.
2. Have the child think of a story or characters (people, animals, or other creatures) that he or she may want to include in a play, and outline each character (from the top of the head to the top of the thighs) on an index card or other piece of card stock.
3. Help the child cut out the character and two finger holes.
4. Have the child insert two fingers in the leg holes and let the action begin.

Tongue Depressor Puppets
Materials
Tongue depressors
Small piece of card stock
(e.g., unlined index cards)
Pencil

Scissors
Colored markers
Tape, glue, or a stapler

Process

1. Make one or two puppets ahead of time to show to the child as an example.
2. Have the child think of a story or characters (people, animals, or other creatures) that he or she may want to include in a play, and outline a character on the card stock.
3. Help the child cut out the character. It may be the character in entirety, its head and trunk, or only its head.
4. Ask the child to use the colored markers to complete the details of the character.
5. Attach the card stock to the tongue depressor with tape, glue, or a stapler.
6. Hold on to the end of the tongue depressor and let the action begin.

07 Light

"Darkness is to space what silence is to sound, i.e., the interval" (McLuhan, 1968). Moments of darkness—intervals in space—can be frightening for children, particularly when they are in unfamiliar surroundings, such as a hospital. Under these circumstances, introducing light can have great meaning. A small flashlight tucked under the pillow to illuminate the darkness when things get scary, a nightlight, a beam of light coming under the door—small yet significant gestures that can make a difference.

Light, a form of energy visible to the human eye, provides an exciting resource for the creation of art. Whether the light is used to create art, or the light is the art itself, children who are ill or hospitalized typically embrace arts experiences that incorporate light and "brighten" their circumstances.

Activities in this section include the use of both old and new technologies. For example, new equipment and techniques make photography a realistic art form to use with children at bedside. Some activities can be used with children of all ages, while one, "Polaroid Image Transfer," should only be used with older children and adolescents, under close supervision.

In the Room

The ideal materials for this activity are a digital camera, laptop computer, and portable printer. However, if time is not critical, any camera and standard film processing can be used. This activity can provide an innovative method for sensitizing children to medical equipment; however, as with any arts activity, the choice of subject matter should always be left up to the child. For best results create some examples to show the child before beginning this activity.

Materials

Digital camera
Laptop computer
Photoshop or other computer program for viewing and printing images
Portable printer (or access to computer, Photoshop, and printer)
Plain paper

Process

1. Point out to the child that there are many interesting things in the room. Explain that some of these things are alike in some way. For example, some items may have similar shapes. Others may share a similar function. For example, a cup, an IV bag, a collection container for a Foley catheter or chest tube all have the ability to hold liquids. Show several examples of photographs of items in a room of your choice, e.g., a room in your home, a classroom, a retail establishment, a healthcare setting.

2. Ask the child to look around the room and to think about a series of items with similar characteristics that he or she would like to photograph. Suggested

characteristics include the following:
- Things with similar shapes
- Things that I don't understand
- Things that I like
- Things that I don't like
- Things that are the same size
- Things that have a similar purpose
- Things that are the same color
- Things from friends or family members
- Things that use electricity
- Things I brought from home
- Things that are disposable

3. Demonstrate the use of the digital camera. Have the child practice taking a few photographs, review the results, and offer pointers if needed.

4. Encourage the child to take photos of as many items that he or she can see that share the selected characteristic.

5. Once shooting is complete, down load the photographs to the computer.

6. Have the child create captions for each photo, if desired.

7. Using Photoshop or another computer program, print the images collectively on one piece of paper or separately on individual paper, following the child's preference.

8. Display the final creation on the child's wall or compile individual papers into book form.

9. Encourage the child to ask others to view the work as it may provide insight into ways the healthcare environment can be altered to be less threatening for the child.

Note: The work of several children can be displayed together in a group show. Exhibits can be par-ticularly effective when the children agree on a simi-lar theme.

what is it?

This activity follows much the same process as "In My Room." And, once again, this activity can provide an innovative method for sensitizing children to medical equipment, but, as with any arts activity, the choice of subject matter should always be left up to the child.

Materials

Digital camera

Laptop computer

Photoshop or other computer program for viewing and printing images

    Portable printer (or access to computer, Photoshop, and printer)

  Plain 8½" X 11" paper

Scissors

Thin foam board or cardboard cut to 8½" X 11"

Hole punch (either a single-, two-, or three-hole punch)

Two or three binder rings

Spray adhesive or rubber cement

Process

1. Before visiting the child, take several ultra-close up photographs of items in a room in a healthcare setting. Some suggestions include close-ups of items such as the corner of a bed rail or the drip chamber of an IV bag. Also photograph the items at a distance to show the entire object in a recognizable format. Print out each image on separate pieces of paper.

2. Show the child the up-close photographs and explain that they are close-up photographs of items that can be found in a healthcare setting and ask him or her to guess what the items are.

3. Discuss with the child that sometimes it is difficult to see the big picture and that sometimes an image only

tells part of the story. After the child has guessed (successfully or unsuccessfully), follow by showing the distance images.

4. Ask the child to look around the room for interesting items to photograph in close-up.

5. With each item identified, discuss with the child angles or points of view that could provide the most interest.

6. Review focus features of the camera and demonstrate as needed.

7. Help the child take a series of photographs of each item up close, from about 3", 6", 12", and 36" and from across the room. Note: Children who are unable to take photographs or only some of them can direct the artist in all aspects of the photo shoot—what to photograph, at what angle, at what distance, etc. The digital camera makes it simple for the artist to verify if the photos are capturing the child's ideas. The artist can snap a photo, have the child view it, save those that meet the child expectations, and delete those that do not.

8. Once shooting is complete, download the photographs to the computer.

9. Using Photoshop or another computer program, print each image separately on individual paper.

10. Explain to the child that you must go outside or to an area with adequate ventilation to adhere the prints to the thin foam board on cardboard.

11. Using the spray adhesive or rubber cement, adhere each photograph to a piece of foam or cardboard.

12. Upon your return, help the child punch at least 2 holes spaced at least 4" apart at the top of each mounted photograph.

13. Help the child arrange each series of photographs in order from the closest up to the greatest distance and insert binder rings to hold them together.

14. View the finished book together and encourage the child to share with staff, family, and friends.

Note: A simpler book can be made by inserting the photos into clear page protectors and attaching together with a ring or displaying in a binder.

Polaroid Image Transfer

Looking for a special activity for adolescents? The process of making Polaroid image transfers is fascinating and, because of the materials used*, should be reserved for older children and adolescents. With this technique, any color Polaroid peel-apart film can be used to create an original print on a range of non-photographic surfaces, such as watercolor paper, fabric, wood veneer, and ceramic tiles.

Below we offer instructions for a simple transfer on wet paper. The result is a unique image, part watercolor part painting and part photography. An excellent source of information on the topic is *Polaroid Image Transfers Tools and Techniques* by Holly Dupre´, 2000, which can be downloaded from her website (http://www.pacificsites.com/~hdupre/trans.html).

Materials
Polaroid camera
Polaroid film
Water bath (a rectangular pan or other container large enough to accommodate the paper, filled with water)
Watercolor paper
Cardstock
Surgical gloves
Squeegee
Brayer

Polaroid Image and Emulsion Transfer by Karen Nichols

Process

1. Explain the process to the child: The film is exposed as normal and pulled from the camera, which spreads the developer across the film. The image dyes begin migrating from the negative to the positive, normally reaching completion in 60 seconds. However, for the transfer process, the film is peeled apart prematurely, after about 15 seconds, which stops the dye migration, leaving the negative with the majority of the dye. The negative is used to create the image.

2. Prepare the paper. Pass the paper through the water bath. Very absorbent paper just requires a quick dip; less absorbent paper should be left in the bath about 5 minutes. Hold the paper above the bath to drain and smooth the paper out on a clean flat surface, such as the child's overbed table. Have the child use the squeegee to remove the excess water. The water will help the paper adhere to the surface to keep it in place.

3. Don gloves (you and the child).

4. Ask the child to take a picture, with the reminder that the process has an overall dulling effect; bright colors will appear less saturated and contrast will be reduced.

5. After exposure, pull the film from the camera.

6. After about 15 seconds, peel the film apart, discard the positive, and place the negative face side down on the prepared paper.

7. Put a piece of cardstock over the negative and ask the child to gently roll the brayer over it for about 1½ minutes to ensure complete contact.

8. Gently peel away the negative in a smooth motion to reveal the transferred image.

* All Polaroid films contain a caustic processing gel that can cause burns on contact with the skin. Surgical gloves should be worn throughout the process and all waste should be disposed of properly.

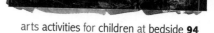

Light Show

Although we use this activity with individual children, our favorite use is with a group of children as a means of fostering community and relieving a sense of isolation. For the most effective light show, have children the decide on a theme (e.g., hospital, season, issue in the news).

Materials

Blank film strip
Paper slide frames
Scissors
Colored markers
Colored tissue and/or construction paper
Flat objects, such as feathers
Glue stick
Iron
Slide projector
Cart

Process

1. Explain to the child that he or she can draw on the film or place some thing (e.g., cut or torn paper, feathers) inside.
2. For drawing, cut a piece of film to fit within the paper slide frame. If the child wants to place something inside, cut two pieces of film.
3. Demonstrate both methods to the child: (a) draw directly on the film with the colored markers, and (b) lightly glue and place torn or cut paper, a feather, or other flat objects on one piece of film and cover with the second piece of film.
4. Ask the child to create a slide.
5. Take the finished artwork and place it within the paper slide frame.
6. With the iron on a low setting, press on the frame to seal the edges.

7. Follow the same procedure with others (i.e., other children, family members, staff).

8. After everyone has had an opportunity to create a slide, fill the slide carousel with all of the slides.

9. Place the slide projector on a cart and move from room to room presenting the completed light show to each child, providing visible proof that indeed he or she is not alone but an active and vibrant part of the hospital community.

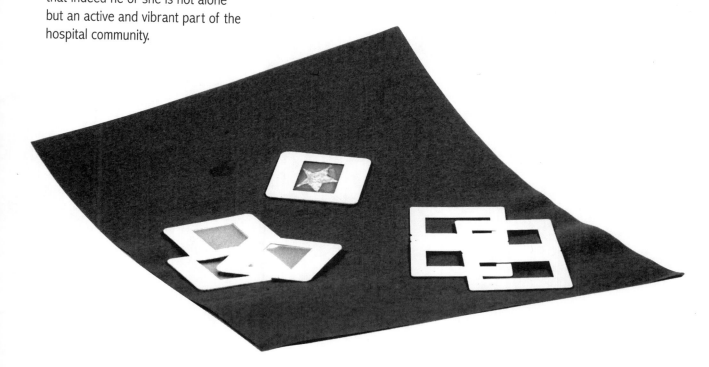

Detail from Nina Favata's "Pegasus"

GlOw in the Dark

For most individuals, children or adults, darkness may be associated with scary thoughts, sounds, and images, especially in a strange environment. With some simple and easy to obtain materials, the darkness can become less frightening for children and something that they may actually welcome. Artist Nina Favata created such an environment in an Emergency X-ray room at Montreal Children's Hospital in Quebec, Canada.

Astrological signs and constellations were researched and chosen to suit the overall flow of the room design. On the defining points of each, Nina painted stars or dots in real gold paint, metallic irridescents mixed with pinks or yellows. On these points she painted many layers of glow-in-the dark paint. This step was done after the room was varnished (Varnish over the glow paint will "deaden" the effect).

The response has been tremendous. Staff members love the room and enjoy working there. They use the constellations to distract anxious children. When a child comes in the room the colors and images are easily visible. However, it is only when the lights are put up for a moment and then way down do they see the constellations emerge as tiny glowing dots! They love it. And staff has a great time playing with the children to find the images that are newly emerging.

Stars are only one option. Children can mix glow-in-the-dark paint to decorate their sleepwear, create mobiles with plastic glow-in-the-dark stars, and produce a variety of other creations.

Materials

Glow in the dark paint
Paintbrush
Glow in the dark objects (stars,
glow sticks, glow tubing)
String, glue, tempera or acrylic paint,
paper, cloth, or other items as the ideas
unfold

Process

1. Ask the child if he or she has ever seen a firefly or "lightening bug" and other things that can been seen at night (e.g., stars, the moon). Depending upon the child's age, discuss the properties of certain materials to "glow in the dark."

2. Explain that the child can transform his or her room to glow in the dark and that what glows can be whatever the child chooses to create.

3. For example, you can review star constellations with the child and suggest that he or she might want to select one to recreate for a personal "night sky," such as the constellation that corresponds to the child's birthday. Some children may want to design their own patterns; of course, the choice is the child's. The child can glue and/or paint stars on poster board, then you can tack or tape the "night sky" above the child's bed.

4. Glow sticks and glow tubing can be used alone or combined with other materials, such as sticks, tree branches, or string to create sculpture.

5. Glow in the dark paint can be applied to T-shirts; girls especially enjoy designing nightshirts using large and extra-large men's sizes.

6. Encourage the child to think of other ways to use this exciting medium.

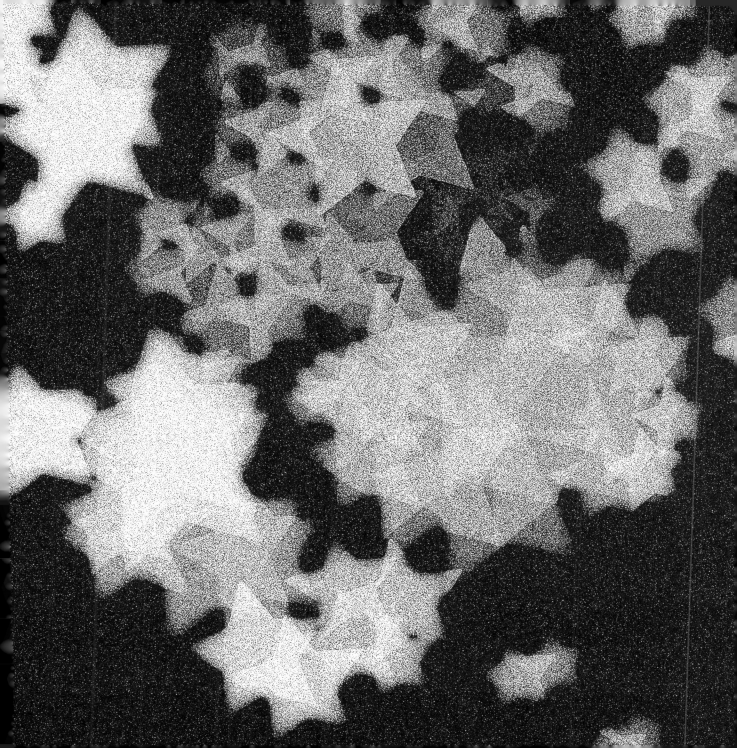

08 Around the World

Learning arts activities from other cultures provides an opportunity for children to celebrate their own culture or to explore the unique contributions made by people from cultures other than their own. For the school aged child, consultation with the child's teacher may result in planning a curriculum-based activity that helps the child keep up with his or her classmates.

Multicultural activities can be based on folk tales, celebrations, arts and crafts, games, music, and dance. Four activities are featured here, but others can be found (e.g., "In the Ring") in other sections of the book.

Child

Clari

East

Emit

Chinese Paper Batiks

This activity is an easier and less expensive version of cloth batiks. Children enjoy the process and the results are beautiful.

Materials
Paper
Crayons
Large paintbrush
Watercolors
Newspaper
Water
Pictures or drawings of the animals listed below (Many Chinese restuarants have placemats with drawings of these animals.)

Process
1. Explain the Chinese calendar to the child, i.e., an animal is assigned a year. Help the child determine his or her animal according to year of birth.

2. Show the child pictures of the animals.

3. Ask the child to draw and color in his or her animal on the piece of paper using the crayons.

4. Once the child has finished drawing, have him or her crumple up the paper into a ball.

5. Run under or submerge the paper ball in cold water and wring out excess.

6. Smooth the paper out on a piece of newspaper.

7. Have the child select a color of paint (dark colors tend to work best) and, using the brush, paint liberally over the paper.

8. Cover the paper with another piece of newspaper, and press down, blotting up the excess water and paint. Repeat as needed until paper is only slightly damp.

9. Let dry.

Note: Children may want to use one of the Kanji symbols or Chinese Zodiac characters pictured on page 106.

Horse—1918-1930-1942-1954-1966-1978-1990-2002
Your capacity for hard work is amazing. You are your own person—very independent. Your sign suggests success as an adventurer, scientist, poet, or politician.

Goat—1919-1931-1943-1955-1967-1979-1991-2003
The Goat can be charming company. You are elegant and artistic but the first to complain about things. You would be best as an actor, gardener, or beachcomber.

Monkey—1920-1932-1944-1956-1968-1980-1992-2004
You are very intelligent, a very clever wit, and always well-liked. Your sign promises success in any field you try.

Rooster—1921-1933-1945-1957-1969-1981-1993-2005
The Rooster is a hard worker, shrewd and definite in decision making, often speaking his or her mind. Born under this sign, you should be happy as a restaurant owner, publicist, soldier, or world traveler.

Dog—1922-1934-1946-1958-1969-1982-1994-2006
The Dog will never let you down. Born under this sign you are honest, and faithful to those you love. You would make an excellent businessman or woman, activist, teacher, or secret agent.

Pig—1923-1935-1947-1959-1970-1983-1995-2007
You are a splendid companion, an intellectual with a very strong need to set difficult goals and carry them out. The Pig would be best in the arts as an entertainer, or possibly a lawyer.

Rat—1924-1936-1948-1960-1971-1984-1996-2008
You are imaginative, charming, and truly generous to the person you love. Born under this sign, you should be happy in sales or as a writer, critic, or publicist.

Buffalo—1913-1925-1937-1949-1961-1972-1985-1997-2009
A born leader, you inspire confidence from all around you. The Buffalo would be successful as a skilled surgeon, general, or hairdresser.

Tiger——1914-1926-1938-1950-1962-1973-1986-1998-2010

You are sensitive, emotional, and capable of great love. Your sign shows you would be excellent as a boss, explorer, race car driver, or matador.

Rabbit——1915-1927-1939-1951-1963-1974-1987-1999-2011

You are the kind of person that people like to be around——affectionate, obliging, always pleasant. You are successful in business, but would also make a good lawyer, diplomat, or actor.

Dragon——1916-1928-1940-1952-1964-1975-1988-2000

You are intelligent, gifted, and a perfectionist, but these qualities make you unduly demanding on others. You would be well-suited to be an artist, priest, or politician.

Snake——1917-1929-1941-1953-1965-1977-1989-2001

Rich in wisdom and charm, you are romantic and deep thinking and your intuition guides you strongly. The Snake would be most content as a teacher, philosopher, writer, psychiatrist, or fortune teller.

Kanji Symbols

Kanji is a Japanese system of writing based on ideographic characters borrowed from the Chinese sometime around the 3rd century. These symbols are graphic representations of words and ideas and carry with them the essence of meaning.

風 Air/Wind | 志 Ambition | 有 Be | 美 Beauty | 生 Birth/Life | 乱 Chaos | 子 Child | 清 Clarity | 慈 Compassion | 英 Courage | 娘 Daughter | 縁 Destiny

信 Devotion | 威 Dignity | 方 Direction | 夢 Dream | 早 Early | 土 Earth | 東 East | 発 Emit | 氣 Energy | 明 Enlightenment | 永 Eternity | 父 Father

風水 Feng Shui | 火 Fire | 恕 Forgiveness | 友 Friends | 先 Future | 順 Gentleness | 華 Glory | 神 God | 福 Good Fortune | 恩 Grace | 化 Growth | 楽 Happy

和 Harmony | 医 Healing | 天 Heaven | 泰 Heaven & Earth | 心 Heart Mind Spirit | 家 Home | 實 Honesty | 貴 Honor | 公 Justice | 気 Ki Chi | 光 Light | 壽 Longevity | 愛 Love

忠 Loyalty | 男 Man | 金 Wealth | 月 Moon | 母 Mother | 新 Now | 北 North | 情 Passion | 去 Past | 忍 Patience | 和 Peace | 孝 Piety | 多 Plenty | 力 Power

洪 Profundity | 粋 Purity | 示 Revelation | 崇 Reverence | 義 Righteousness | 聖 Sage | 海 Sea | 直 Simplicity | 誠 Sincerity | 伜 Son | 南 South | 間 Space Between

気 Spirit | 岩 Stone | 話 Story | 強 Strong | 日 Sun | 道 Tao | 教 Teacher | 思 Think | 旅 Travel | 真 Truth | 安 Tranquility | 会 Understanding | 協 Unity

健 Vigor | 德 Virtue | 水 Water | 西 West | 智 Wisdom | 幸 Wish | 女 Woman | 木 Wood | 書 Write

Chinese Zodiac

鼠 Rat | 牛 Ox | 虎 Tiger | 兔 Hare | 龍 Dragon | 蛇 Serpent | 馬 Horse | 羊 Ram | 猴 Monkey | 雞 Rooster | 犬 Dog | 豬 Boar

Japanese Garden Theatre

Hiromi Moriguchi of Tanpopo-No-Ye, Nara, Japan, introduced us to this creative activity, which is a little different from gardening therapy (Hiromi, 2004). In garden theatre, children can create their own soil-less environment for creatures to roam, play, and interact—sort of a Japanese version of sandtray. An added benefit: children can actually watch something grow and change over time. Garden theatres can be very simple with just a stick or two of bamboo, or quite elaborate with orchids.

Materials

A flat, shallow bowl or watertight tray
Rocks
Bamboo
Other plants as desired
Small figures (purchased or handmade)

Process

1. Have the child place two or three layers of rocks in the bottom of the bowl.
2. Pour in enough water just until you can see it coming through the rocks.
3. Have the child place the bamboo where desired.
4. Ask the child to turn the creatures loose in the "garden" and let the action begin. The child creates a story and expresses the story inside the miniature garden.
5. At another time, have the child find or create other items, such as small houses, and add them to the garden.
6. Maintain the garden by adding more water when needed.

Note: The child may also want to write and illsutrate a script for his or her "play." Background music may be used as well.

AbOriginal Dreamtime Painting

We have used this activity, which is popular with children at the annual Melbourne Show in Victoria, Australia, very successfully with children at bedside. "Tjukurpa" or "Dreamtime" for Aboriginals in Australia was creation time when ancestral beings emerged from the earth. Although they resembled plants and animals, they were part human. They behaved like human beings—hunting, fighting, loving, hating—as they journeyed across the land. They made the law and from their deeds Aboriginal people learned the proper way to behave and to live with each other. Once they tired of their life, these mythical creatures disappeared underground again. Dreamtime means existence in the past, present, and future (Stokes, 1992).

Aboriginals relate the stories of their ancestors through Dreamtime paintings, sometimes called "dot paintings," using certain symbols (see "Symbols of Dreamtime Art"). Symbols of Dreamtime art can be read in many ways; thus, even the secret, sacred parts of a Dreaming can be drawn but still remain hidden. Only the artist fully understands the meaning.

Materials
Black construction paper
Oil-based pastels
Examples of symbols

Process
1. Tell the story of Aboriginal Dreamtime.*
2. Show the child the symbols of Dreamtime art on the following page and discuss the meanings of the symbols.

3. Using a piece of black construction paper and the oil-based pastels, demonstrate how to make the symbols using dots.
4. Giving examples, discuss how the child can combine the symbols to create his or her own story.
5. Hand the child a piece of black construction paper and the oil-based pastels to develop a story.
6. Give the child the option of either telling you the story or keeping the meaning of the Dreamtime drawing a secret.

* This is a wonderful activity to do in collaboration with a storyteller. An excellent book on the topic is *Desert Dreamings* by Dierdre Stokes, 1992, Milton, Queensland, Australia: The Jacaranda Press.

travelling   resting place

rain

water
snakes
smoke

campsite
well
stone
hole
fruit

 man

star

kangaroo

rainbow
cloud
cliff

four women sitting

French Divisionalism

Unlike some drawing or painting activities, this torn paper technique requires very little skill to have excellent results. Based on the French painter Georges Seurat's divisionism painting method yet not as disciplined, bits of colored paper are applied to create very simple or complex images—the child's choice.

Materials

White drawing or painting paper or card stock
Pencil
A full range of colored construction paper
Glue and a small container
Paintbrush

Process

1. Show the child a picture of a Seurat's painting where he used his divisionism technique, such as "A Sunday on La Grande Jattee." See The Art Insitute of Chicago's website (http://www.artic.edu/artaccess/AA_Impressionist/pages/IMP_7.shtml) for the image as well as addition information about Seurat and divisionism.

2. Have the child take a close look and point out that the painting consists of many small dots of paint.

3. Explain that artists can "paint" with paper as well.

4. Hand the child a piece of white paper and a pencil.

5. Have the child look around the room or out the window or use his or her imagination to think of an object or scene to depict. As an alternative, set up a still life, using objects the child suggests.

6. Ask the child to draw a simple line drawing to outline major objects of the image. Explain that it is best to keep things very simple at this point.

7. When the basic structure is in place, ask the child to select the colors of paper for "painting." Encourage the use of variations of the same color for depicting shadows or light on objects.

8. Help the child tear pieces of colored construction paper into about ½" pieces. Family members can help out with this step as well.

9. Pour glue into a container and demonstrate the application of color:
   - Brush a small amount of glue on a small section of a white piece of paper.
   - Apply the bits of colored paper to create the images.
   - Explain that it is important to overlap the bits of paper so that none of the white paper is visible.

10. Have the child continue until the entire white paper is covered. The child may wish to work on this project over time rather than complete it in one session.

Note: An alternative method is dipping the end of wine corks into thickened tempera paint and making various colored dots on the paper.

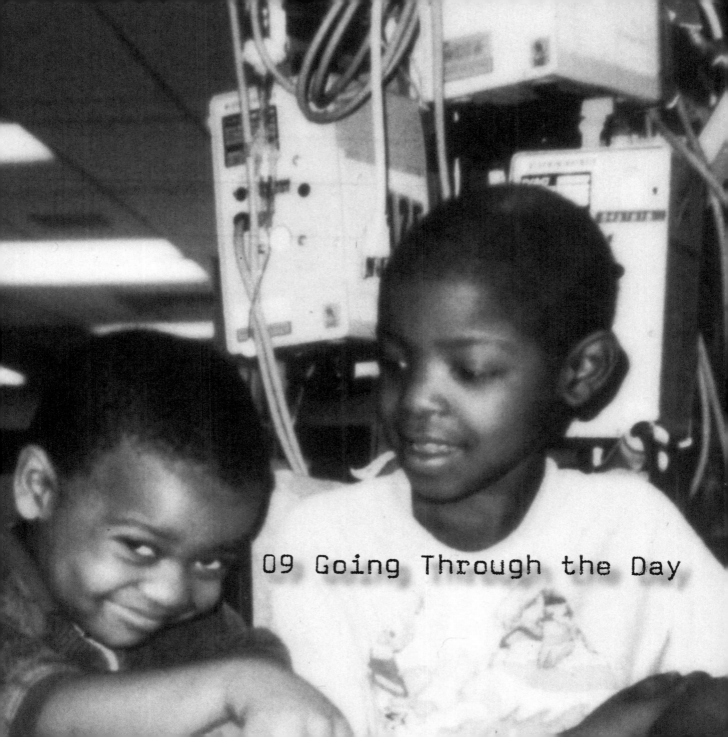

09 Going Through the Day

This book would be incomplete without mentioning the opportunities that parents, nurses, child life specialists, play specialists, social workers, chaplains, and other caregivers have to bring the arts to children at bedside. Granted, most parents and professional caregivers are not artists, musicians, storytellers, etc. Never the less, caring individuals can incorporate simple arts activities into care-giving routines and bring joy, laughter, and many of the physiologic benefits that professional artists bring.

The arts can accompany the daily routines that all children experience, such as mealtime, bath time, and bedtime, as well as treatment routines that children, especially those with chronic conditions, experience. Music has proven beneficial in establishing treatment routines as positive experiences for children and their families (Grasso, Button, Allison, & Sawyer, 2000). For example, routine chest physiotherapy (CPT) for children with cystic fibrosis requires a significant commitment of time and energy. Grasso and colleagues compared the use of newly composed music, familiar music, and the family's usual routine on children's and parents' enjoyment of CPT and found that children's and parents' enjoyment of CPT significantly increased after the use of specifically composed and recorded music as an adjunct.

An excellent resource for play activities to use throughout the day with children is *Therapeutic Play Activities for Hospitalized Children* developed by a team representing child life, nursing, and psychology (Hart et al., 1992) (see references for details). Many of these play activities incorporate the arts or can be adapted to include art modalities.

This final section begins with the use of the arts in daily care and at mealtime. We then offer simple ways to incorporate the arts into the medical environment. We conclude by presenting an easy method to obtain meaningful information to help children develop coping strategies to deal with stressful treatment experiences, as well as some suggestions for helping children cope with a sampling of treatment regimes.

Daily Care

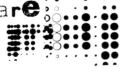

The arts are easy to incorporate into a child's daily care. Although music is probably the easiest, other art forms may be used as well during bathing, dressing, or other daily care activities.

Embedded Handmade Soap

Soap with a toy inside makes bath time fun, especially when children make the soap themselves. Glycerin-based soap is easy for children to use and safe for their skin. Below are instructions for a simple clear soap. However, if the child's condition permits, colors and fragrances may be added. These items as well as glycerin-based melt and pour soap base are readily available at craft stores and via the web.

Materials
Microwave*
Microwave safe container (a glass Pyrex® measuring cup works well)
4 oz of clear glycerin-based melt and pour soap base
Plastic container (storage container, ice cube tray) to serve as a mold
Spoon or chopstick
Small vinyl toys or colorful erasers

Process
1. Have the child put chunks of the soap base into a microwave safe container.
2. Microwave for about 50 seconds.
3. Using a spoon or chopstick, gently swirl until all is melted. Do not stir vigorously or the soap will foam.
4. Help the child pour a very thin layer of the soap base into the plastic container.

5. Once the soap base has set, have the child choose toys and/or erasers and place them in the container on top of the soap base.
6. Help the child pour another layer of soap to fill the rest of the mold.
7. When the soap has set up, put the mold into a freezer for about 20 minutes.
8. Once chilled, invert the mold and give it a gentle twist. The soap will be released.

*Note: For room-to-room visits, an electric frying pan filled with about an inch of water and an empty clean coffee can may be used as a double boiler to melt the soap base. Be sure to bring along a potholder as the coffee can will get hot.

Other Ideas

The following list of ideas to incorporate in daily care is designed to stimulate your imagination.

1. Make up a song together about what you and the child like and dislike, such as "My name is <u>Maria</u> and I like <u>swimming</u>."
2. Make up a song together about what the weather is like today.
3. Make up a song together about water and soap.
4. Make up a song together using words that rhyme with the child's name.

5. Sing the "Hokey Pokey" and have the child move an arm, leg, etc., when it is time to wash or clothe that part of the body.

6. Play recorded music of the child's choice.

7. Use a song as a timing devise, e.g., "Let's see if we can finish your bath before the song ends."

8. Create a sculptural "masterpiece" with the child's hair while shampooing.

9. Make up a special song for brushing teeth.

10. Search a children's songbook for songs about bathing and dressing, such as "One, two, buckle my shoe."

11. Create a simple puppet from a wash cloth for the child to use while bathing.

12. Have the child create a special bath towel using colored markers for fabrics.

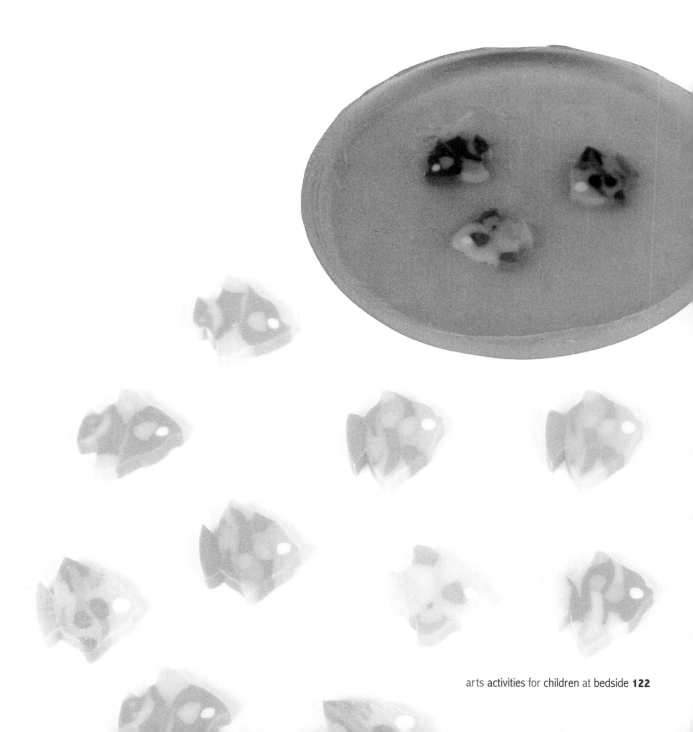

Mealtime

Children who are ill often need encouragement to eat. Below we offer three activities that require very little in the way of materials or execution that may help children look forward to mealtime.

The Muffin Man

A combination music/visual arts project turns mealtime into a special event for small children.

Materials
Paper napkin
1 piece of white paper 8½" X 11"
Scissors
Stapler

Process
1. Cut the piece of paper in half length wise.
2. Fold each piece in half lengthwise.
3. Staple the two pieces together to form one long band.
4. Encircle the child's head with the band to size.
5. Staple the other ends of the band together to close the circle. This will serve as the base for the "Muffin Man" hat.
6. Unfold the paper napkin.
7. Staple each of the four corners to the inside of the band at four points (at 9, 12, 3, and 6 o'clock).
8. Place the hat on the child's head and sing "The Muffin Man."

The Muffin Man

Do you know the Muffin Man, the Muffin
Man, the Muffin Man
Do you know the Muffin Man, who lives on
Drury Lane?

Why yes, I know the Muffin Man, the Muffin
Man, the Muffin Man,
Why yes, I know the Muffin Man, who lives
on Drury Lane.

Pudding Fingerpainting

Although pudding is a favorite for this
activity, foods with similar properties, such
as yogurt, may also be used.

Materials

Pudding (prepared)
Smooth washable tray
Spoon

Process

1. Spoon prepared pudding on tray.
2. With your fingers, demonstrate how
   to draw in the pudding.
3. Encourage the child to draw in the
   pudding.
4. Add different flavors (colors) of
   pudding to offer variety and to
   provide opportunities for
   blending colors.
5. Encourage the child to taste while
   creating, and to consume the
   creation when complete.

Puppy Salad

Fruits and vegetables serve as wonderful
materials to create an animal salad. The
following is an example of an easy-to-
make healthy fruit salad. Help the child do
as many of the steps as possible.

Materials

1 pear
1 large strawberry
2 raisons
Lettuce
Plate
Knife

Process

1. Have the child place a layer of
   lettuce on the plate.
2. Hollow out two small holes in the
   pear for the eyes.
3. Place the pear on the lettuce and ask
   the child to put a raison into each of
   the holes.

4. Ask the child to place the strawberry halves on the side of the puppy's head to form the ears.

5. You might want to help the child photograph the puppy before serving.

The Medical Environment

Medical equipment and the healthcare environment can be frightening for children. The arts can be used to "soften" medical equipment, to make it more familiar and less threatening to children.

IV Pump Pal
Materials
Magazines or books with pictures of animals
Colored construction paper
Fabric
Large black mailing labels
Feathers
Pipe cleaners
Colored markers
Other found objects
Scissors
Masking tape
String or yarn
Glue

Process
1. Explain that it is easy to turn an IV pump into an animal friend.
2. Show the child the magazines or books with pictures of animals and ask him or her to select one.
3. Choosing from available materials, help the child decorate portions of the pole, using the pump itself as the trunk of the animal (avoid putting anything on the front of the pump). For example, a bird's head can be fashioned from construction paper and hung from the pole with string. Feathers can be glued to construction paper and taped to the side of the pump for wings.
4. Children with low energy levels may want to simply create some stickers using colored markers (or direct you in creating them), and apply them to the pump.

IV Mandalas

This is a favorite activity that artist-in-residence Joan Drescher uses with children at MassGeneral Hospital for Children in Boston, MA.

Materials

Cardboard pizza rounds (try a local food distributor)
Crayons, colored markers, paints
Tissue paper
Feathers
Glitter
Glue
Pipe cleaners
Ribbons
Other found materials
One-hole punch

Process

1. With the pizza cardboard round, demonstrate making a mandala, explaining that the child can begin by creating a border and work inward, begin at the center and work outward, or just begin wherever he or she chooses.
2. Offer the child a wide range of media and assist as needed. The child may create realistic or abstract images.
3. When finished, using the one-hole punch, have the child punch a hole near the edge.
4. Insert a pipecleaner in the hole.
5. Hang the mandala by the pipe cleaner over the top of the IV pole.

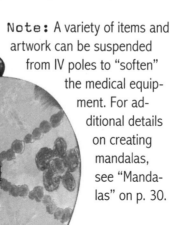

Note: A variety of items and artwork can be suspended from IV poles to "soften" the medical equipment. For additional details on creating mandalas, see "Mandalas" on p. 30.

"Stained Glass" Windows

This is another of Joan Drescher's favorite activities to empower children to change their environment and thus help them cope with illness and/or hospitalization. The window resembles stained glass when the sun shines through the child's creations.

Materials

Coffee filters
Bingo bottles (small plastic bottles with a sponge top) filled with different colors of liquid watercolor or water-based dyes
Newspaper
Tape

Process

1. Spread out some newspaper on the work surface.
2. Hand the child several coffee filters.
3. Demonstrate folding a filter in half, then in half again two to three more times.
4. Have the child use the colors of watercolor or dye of choice to stain various parts of the coffee filter. Coffee filters are absorbent so the colors will bleed together. The dye will leak through to the surfaces of the filter underneath.
5. Ask the child to open the filter to see the pattern that's been created.
6. Repeat this process until the child has completed the number of filters desired.
7. Allow the filters to dry and then tape to the child's window.
8. Encourage the child to focus on these images during procedures, treatments, or times of discomfort.

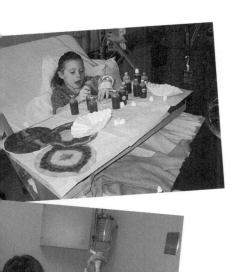

The Hardest Part

The Hardest Part is a simple drawing technique for children to use for reappraisal of reoccurring stressful events or treatment regimes, as things that are scary or confusing are often difficult to put into words. The technique works well for general chronic stressors, such as dealing with the side effects of chemotherapy, and distinct, time-limited stressors, such as a lumbar puncture. It is inappropriate and probably impossible to force children to process an experience until they are ready. However, it is important to offer children the opportunity to do so. Accompanying this opportunity with materials to draw may increase the likelihood that the processing will take place. Successful processing with a caring person and reappraisal can result in the child's voice being heard and our learning the most meaningful ways to meet his or her needs.

Materials

Paper

Pencil, pen, colored markers, or crayons

Process

1. Provide the child with paper and a pencil or other drawing implement.
2. Ask the child to draw a picture of the hardest part of dealing with _____ _____ (the stressor—chemotherapy, dressing changes, etc.).
3. After the child has completed the drawing, ask, "Would you like to tell me about your drawing?"
4. As the child responds, provide specific positive feedback to the child so that the child can explore what he or she did that was effective in coping for consideration for use the next time. For example, if the child draws and says that the hardest part was holding still, acknowledge how important yet difficult it is to hold still, and praise the child for doing so. This provides concrete and specific feedback about what doing a "great job" entails.

5. When the child has not coped effectively, use the valuable information—what the child found most difficult about the experience—to help the child build effective coping strategies, perhaps using music, singing, storytelling, or other arts modalities, to address the "hardest part" for future experiences.

Note: A similar stratgey may be used to prepare a child for an event by asking, "What do you think the hardest part will be for you?"

Treatment Regimes

A treatment regime often is a very significant part of a child's day. We have addressed incorporating the arts with some of the more common ones that children in healthcare settings experience.

IV Garden

Therapeutic horticulture is the purposeful use of plants and plant-related activities to promote health and wellness for an individual or group and has been shown to be extremely valuable and effective in health care settings for very ill children. A small indoor garden can benefit children on many levels. Gardening offers stress relief; plants and gardens impart a sense of the natural rhythm of life. It can offer a distraction. Children can create and control a part of their environment, which is empowering. Stimulating all of the senses, gardening gives great pleasure and satisfaction and promotes eye-hand coordination, range-of-motion, and endurance.

The following activity incorporates the use of medical equipment with therapeutic horticulture. This activity is especially appropriate for children who have had IVs, are chronically ill or disabled, and/or those with a lengthy convalescence.

Materials
Recycled used IV bag and tubing
Plant or plants
Container
Soil
Water

Process
1. Help the child pot a plant of choice in the container.
2. Discuss the care of the plant, e.g., the need for water, sunlight.

3. Fill a recycled IV bag with water. Plant food may be added if appropriate.
4. Attach recycled tubing and close the flow regulator.
5. Hang the IV bag with tubing above the plant on an IV pole, wall or ceiling hook, etc.
6. Demonstrate how to regulate the flow of water with the regulator and let the child practice.
7. Discuss a care plan for the plant, including refilling the bag from time to time, and encourage the child to accept as much responsibility for its care as possible.

Among the Stars

This activity, adapted from "Magic Bottles" by Hart and colleagues (1992), can be incorporated into preparing children for procedures. The bottle or jar can be used as a visual distraction during the procedure or treatment and/or to help deal with discomfort afterwards.

Materials

An empty spring water bottle or any empty clear bottle or jar

Mineral oil
Funnel
Metallic stars
Glitter
Water
Blue or purple food coloring
Duct tape

Process

1. Show the child an Among the Stars bottle that you have made ahead of time. Shake it gently and discuss how the stars move throughout the bottle.
2. Have the child place the funnel in the bottle's mouth.
3. Ask the child to fill the bottle halfway with mineral oil.
4. Have the child add metallic stars and glitter.
5. Ask the child to add enough water to within ½" of the top.
6. Have the child add blue or purple food coloring.
7. Remove the funnel and screw the top on tightly. Use duct tape to further secure the top to the bottle.

8. Have the child gently shake the bottle and watch the movement of the stars. Explain that the child can enter his or her own personal galaxy and focus on the stars during procedures, treatments, or periods of discomfort.

A Day In the Life Of..

A child's daily routine often can be quite complex. Creating a series of storyboards can serve as a coping strategy by providing visual acknowledgement of the challenges that a child faces each day. Discussion around the project can also provide an opportunity to identify the parts of the routine that are most difficult for the child, and thus provide a focus for problem solving with the child, family, and healthcare team.

Some children may need to create additional storyboards to tell their story, so it is good to have additional poster board on hand. If a video camera is available, the activity can be extended into actually having children film their day.

Materials
3 sheets of poster board
Scissors
Paper and pen or pencil
Colored markers
Masking tape or a one-hole punch and a binder ring

Process
1. Explain to the child that storyboards are used as a basis for making films, and that he or she can develop storyboards about a day in his or her life.
2. Fold sheets of poster board in half and cut along the fold.
3. Fold those pieces in half and cut along the folds. You will now have four pieces of poster board. Prepare the other sheets in the same manner.
4. With the child, review the child's daily routine and list the events on the paper.
5. Encourage the child to think of images to use to illustrate the events.
6. Ask the child to use the markers to illustrate each event on the pieces of poster board, numbering each

board to indicate where the event falls in the sequence of the day.

7. Post the storyboards to the child's wall with the masking tape or attach together by punching a hole in a corner of each board and inserting a ring.

8. Follow up by asking the child to discuss the contents of each storyboard to assess the child's perceptions about each event of the day. Use this information as a basis for working together to develop coping strategies for dealing with the difficult parts.

Other Simple Activities to Promote TreatmentGoals

1. To encourage deep breathing
   - Tell the story "The Three Little Pigs" and have the child join in with "I'll huff and I'll puff and I'll blow your house down."
   - Sing a song about bubbles and have the child blow bubbles as an accompaniment.

2. To encourage range of motion
   - Tell a story and have the child dramatize the actions.

- Ask the child to imitate the movements of animals in a story.
- Have the child create figures or other sculptures with clay.

3. To encourage soaking of an extremity
   - Put small colored objects such as plastic blocks or poker chips into the bottom of a soaking bowl or pan and ask the child to move them about with the hand or foot to create an underwater scene.
   - Put plastic workers in the water and ask the child to act out a play of the workers building a railroad while singing "I've Been Working on the Railroad."
   - Put plastic farm animals in the water and ask the child to have them dance to the tune of "Old MacDonald Had a Farm."

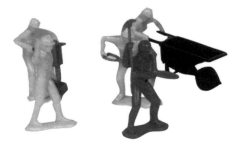

<<A Final Note>>

We hope that you have found among these pages an idea or two to try with children who are ill, disabled, or hospitalized. But perhaps as important, we would like most of all to believe that this book might have stimulated the imagination—both yours and the children you serve—and broadened your expectations about the exciting role the arts can play, even when a child is confined to bed.

The arts offer a powerful box of tools that enable the child's voice to be heard. Artists, healthcare professionals, parents, and other concerned and trusted adults can help assure that children have these critical tools available to help them navigate the difficult challenges inherent in children's healthcare settings and to celebrate the good things that occur in such settings as well.

Children tell us, and research confirms, that connected relationships—where adults in their lives think of them as people first and "patients" second, are very important in helping them cope with the stresses of illness and treatment (Rollins, 2003). A significant feature of these relationships is flexibility—being able to surprise, bend the rules. Thus, as ideas spring forth, the question to ask is not "Why?" but "Why not?" For instance, why not bring in a tub of snow for children to create snow sculptures? There may be many good reasons "why not" for a particular child at a particular time. But, if after exploring and addressing the "becauses" and coming up with no good reason "why not", perhaps it is time to figure out a way to make it happen.

Human relationships are primary in all of living. In the words of Fred Rogers (2003, p. 94), "When the gusty winds blow and shake our lives, if we know that people care about us, we may bend with the wind...but we won't break."

A creative partnership between you and the children you serve and care about can lead to exciting possibilities beyond anything that any of you can accomplish alone. Go forth together and create some great memories.

References

Banks, S., Davis, P., Howard, V., & McLaughlin, T. (1993). The effects of directed art activities on the behavior of young children with disabilities: A multi-element baseline analysis. *Art Therapy: Journal of the American Art Therapy Association, 10* (4), 235–240.

Bursill, H. 1993). *Hand shadows to be thrown upon the wall: A series of novel and amusing figures formed by the hand* (2nd ed.). London: Griffith and Farran.

Dion, S. (2000). *Write now: Maintaining a creative spirit while homebound and ill.* Teaneck, NJ: The Puffin Foundation, Ltd.

Dupre´, H. (2000). *Polaroid image transfers tools and techniques.* Retrieved on August 23, 2003 from http://www.pacificsites.com/~hdupre/trans.html

Edwards, B. (1999). *Drawing on the right side of the brain.* New York: HarperCollins.

Fincher, S. (1991). *Creating mandalas for insight, healing, and self-expression.* Boston: Shambhala.

Grasso, M., Button, B., Allison, D., & Sawyer, S. (2000). Benefits of music therapy as an adjunct to chest physiotherapy in infants and toddler with cystic fibrosis. *Pediatric Pulmonology, 29* (5), 371-381.

Greaves, R. (1994). *Child art: A parents' handbook* (2nd ed.). Victoria, Australia: Art Craft Teachers' Association Inc.

Hart, R., Mather, P., Slack, J., & Powell, M. (1992). *Therapeutic play activities for hospitalized children.* St. Louis: Mosby Year Book.

Hilgard, J., & LeBaron, S. (1984). *Hypnotherapy of pain in children with cancer.* Los Altos, CA: William Kaufman.

Hiromi, M. (2004). Studies on "Caring for the caregiver," the current situations of social welfare workers in Japan. In L. Kable, (Ed.), *Caring for caregivers: A grassroots USA-Japan initiative* (pp. 31-33). Washington, DC: Society for the Arts in Healthcare.

Johnson, L. (1997). *The Life Necklace: Celebrating the creativity of children in hospitals.* Washington, DC: Rollins & Associates, Inc.

Kline, N. (2002). Prevention and treatment of infections. In C. Baggott, K. Kelly, D. Fochtman, & G. Foley (Eds.), *Nursing care of children and adolescents with cancer* (3rd ed.). Philadelphia: W.B. Saunders.

McCraty, R., Barrios-Choplin, B, Atkinson, M., & Tomasino, D. (1998). The effects of different types of music on mood, tension, and mental clarity. *Alternative Therapies in Health and Medicine,* 4(1), 75–84.

McLuhan, H.M. (1968). *Toward a spacial dialogue.* New York: HarperCollins.

Olds, A. (1987). *Child healthcare facilities.* Washington, DC: Association for the Care of Children's Health.

Prescott, E., & David, T. (1976). *The effects of the physical environment on day care.* Pasadena, CA: Pacific Oaks College.

Rice, G. (2003). *A poet in the practice?* The role of the arts in health care. Accessed January 11, 2004, from http://www.bristolmedchi.co.uk/-doctor/1.Clinical%20Topics.html#poet

Roche, N. (1991). *The new clay: Techniques and approaches to jewelry making.* Gaithersburg, MD: Flower Valley Press, Inc.

Rogers, F. (2003). *The world according to Mister Rogers: Important things to remember.* New York: Hyperion.

Rollins, J. (2003). A comparison of stress and coping for children with cancer in the United Kingdom and the United States. Unpublished doctoral dissertation, DeMontfort University, Leicester, England.

Rollins, J. (in press). The arts in children's healthcare settings. In J. Rollins, R. Bolig, & C. Mahan (Eds.), *Meeting children's psychosocial needs across the healthcare continuum.* Austin TX: ProEd, Inc.

Schroeder-Sheker, T. (1993). Music for the dying: A personal account of the new field of music thanatology—history, theories, and clinical narratives. *ADVANCES, The Journal of Mind-body Health, 9* (1), 36–48.

Stokes, D. (1992). *Desert dreamings.* Milton, Queensland, Australia: The Jacaranda Press.

The Pew-Fetzer Task Force. (1995). *Health professions and relationship-centered care.* San Francisco, CA: The Pew Health Professions Commission.

Ulrich, R. (1984). View through window may influence recovery from surgery. *Science, 224,* 420-421.

Wikoff, N. (2003). From the president. *SAH News, 13* (2), 1.

Appendix A
A Selection of Ethnic and Religious Festivals

January	February	March
New Year's Day—1 Japanese New Year St. Basil's Day (Greece)—1 Yuan Tan (Chinese New Year)—between January 21 and February 19 Mardi Gras (France, French communities)—January or February	Feast Day of St. Brigid (Ireland)—1 Tet (Vietnam New Year)—January or February	Nigeria (Ibo people) New Year Iranian New Year Clear and Bright Festival (China)—Late March or early April St. Patrick's Day (Ireland)—17 Easter (Christian communities)—March or April Passover (Jewish communities)—March or April Holi (Hindu)
April	May	June
Burmese New Year Bangladesh New Year Flower Festival (Japan)—8 Verrazano Day (Italy)—17	Tulip Festival (Netherlands) Children's Day (Japan)—5 Cinco de Mayo—5 Norway's Constitution Day (Scandinavia)—17	Republic, or Constitution Day (Italy)—2 Swedish Flag Day (Scandinavian)—6 Festival of John the Baptist (Puerto Rico)—23

July	August	September
Dominion Day (Canada)—1 Independence Day (United States)—4 Bastille Day (France)—14 Festival of Loiza Aldea (Puerto Rico)—25–28	Warsaw Uprising Day (Poland)—1	Rosh Hashanah (Jewish New Year) Ghana's (Eve People) New Year Ethiopia's New Year Tet Trung (Vietnam)—September or October Yom Kippur (Jewish communities)—September or October Durga Puja (Hindu) Mexican Independence Day (Mexico)—16 Native American Indian Day (United States)—4th Friday
October	November	December
Octoberfest (Germany) Leif Eriksson Day (Scandinavia)—9 Pulaski Day (Poland)—11 Divali (Hindu)—October or November	Guy Fawkes Day (England)—5 St. Martin Day (Germany)—11 Thanksgiving Day (United States)—4th Thursday	Our Lady of Guadeloupe Day (Mexico)—12 Hanukkah (Jewish communities) Christmas Day (Christian communities)—25 Kwanzaa (African Americans)—25–31

Appendix B
Art Materials and Projects for Children and Other High-Risk Individuals

Children under age twelve or who are intellectually or physically disabled, the chronically ill, elderly people, and others at elevated risk from exposure to toxic chemicals can replace toxic materials with safer ones.

DO NOT USE	SUBSTITUTES
Solvents and Solvent-Containing Products	*Water-Based and Solvent-Free Products*
1. Alkyd, oil enamels, or other solvent-containing paints.	Acrylics, oil sticks, water-based paints, watercolors, or other water-based paints containing safe pigments.
2. Turpentine, paint thinners, citrus solvents, or other solvents for cleaning up or thinning oil paints.	Mix oil-based, solvent-free paints with linseed oil only. Clean brushes with baby oil followed by soap and water.
3. Solvent-based silkscreen inks and other printing inks containing solvents or requiring solvents for cleanup.	Use water-based silkscreen, block printing, or stencil inks with safe pigments.
4. Solvent-containing varnishes, mediums, and alcohol-containing shellacs.	Use acrylic emulsion coatings, or the teacher can apply it for students under proper conditions.
5. Rubber cement and thinners for paste-up and mechanicals.	Use low-temperature wax methods, double-sided tape, glue sticks, or other solvent-free materials.

6. Airplane glue and other solvent-containing glues.	Use methyl cellulose glues, school paste, glue sticks, preservative-free wheat paste, and solvent-free glues.
7. Permanent felt-tip markers, white-board markers, and other solvent-containing markers.	Use water-based markers or chalk.

Powdered Dusty Materials	*Dustless Products or Processes*
1. Clay from mixing dry clay, sanding greenware, other dusty processes.	Purchase talc-free, low silica, premixed clay. Trim clay when leather-hard, clean up often during work. Practice good hygiene and dust control.
2. Ceramic glaze dust from mixing ingredients, applying, and other processes.	Do not use even lead-free glazes in grade 6 or under. Substitute with paints. The teacher can seal the paints with water-based acrylic varnish.
3. Metal enamel dust. Even lead-free enamels contain other toxic metals, and avoiding enamels altogether will eliminate the dangerous heat and acids involved in the enameling process.	Substitute with paints.
4. Powered tempera and other powdered paints.	Purchase premixed paints, or have the teacher mix them.

5. Powered dyes for batik, tie-dying, other textile processes.	Use vegetable and plant materials (e.g., onion skins, tea), FDA-approved food dyes, or unsweetened Kool-Aid.
6. Plaster dust. Do not sand plaster or do other dusty work. To avoid burns, do not cast hands or other body parts in plaster.	Have teachers premix plaster outdoors or in local exhaust ventilation. Cut rather than tear plaster-impregnated casting cloth.
7. Instant papier-mache dust from finely ground magazines, newspapers, etc.	Use pieces of plain paper or black-and-white newspaper with methyl cellulose glues, paste, or other safe glues.
8. Pastels, chalks, or dry markers that create dust.	Use oil pastels or sticks, crayons, and dustless chalks.

Aerosols and Spray Products	*Liquid Materials*
1. Spray paints, fixatives, etc.	Use water-based liquids that are brushed, dripped, or splattered on, or have the teacher use sprays in local exhaust ventilation or outdoors.
2. Airbrushes.	Replace with other paint methods. Mist should not be inhaled, and airbrushes can be misused.

Miscellaneous Products	Substitutes
1. All types of professional artist's materials.	Use products approved and recommended for children when teaching children or high-risk adults.
2. Toxic metals such as arsenic, lead, cadmium, lithium, barium, chrome, nickel, vanadium, manganese, antimony, etc. These are common ingredients in ceramic glazes, enamels, paints, and many art materials.	Only use materials found free of highly toxic substances.
3. Epoxy resins, instant glues, or plastic resin adhesives.	Use methyl cellulose, library paste, or glue sticks.
4. Plastic resin casting systems or preformed plastics.	Use only preformed plastics, and use them in ways that do not involve heat, solvents, or any other method that will release vapors, gases, and odors.
5. Acid etches and pickling baths.	Do not use.
6. Bleach for reverse dyeing of fabric or colored paper.	Do not use. Thinned white paint can be used to simulate bleach on colored paper.
7. Photographic chemicals.	Use blueprint paper to make sun-grams or use Polaroid cameras. Be sure students do not abuse Polaroid film or pictures, which contain toxic chemicals.

8. Stained-glass projects using lead, solder, or glass cutting.	Use colored cellophane and black paper or tape to simulate stained glass. Or use plastic came to set plastic pieces. Teachers can glue it in a ventilated area.
9. Industrial talcs contaminated with asbestos or nonfibrous asbestos minerals used in many white clays, slip-casting clays, glazes, French chalk, and parting powders.	Use other, talc-free products.
10. Sculpture stones contaminated with asbestos such as some soapstones, steatites, serpentines, etc.	Always use stones found free of asbestos on analysis.
11. Face and skin painting/tattooing with art paints or markers that are not labeled and approved for this use.	Always use products approved for use on the skin (e.g., cosmetics or colored sunscreen creams).
12. Scented markers.	Do not use. These teach children to sniff art markers.
13. Random assortments of plants and seeds.	Identify all plants to be sure no toxic or sensitizing plants are used (e.g., poison oak, castor, etc.).
14. Donated, found, or old materials whose ingredients are unknown.	Use clean, unused materials. Products used with food or other animal or organic materials may harbor bacteria or other hazardous microbes (e.g., washed plastic meat trays may harbor salmonella).

Note. From "The Artist's Complete Health and Safety Guide (3rd ed.)" by M. Rossol, 2001, New York: Alworth Press, pp. 366–369. Reprinted with permission.

Judy Rollins, PhD, RN, Director
of Research and Program
Development, WVSA arts
connection, is a nurse with a fine
arts degree in the visual arts,
an MS in child development
and family studies, and a PhD
in health and community studies.
She is an adjunct Instructor in the
Department of Family Medicine
at Georgetown University School
of Medicine in Washington, DC,
and associate editor of *Pediatric
Nursing*. Dr. Rollins consults, writes,
and researches on children's issues,
with a special interest in the use of
the arts for children in healthcare
settings and a focus on children with
cancer and their families.

NOTES